G000078406

Collins

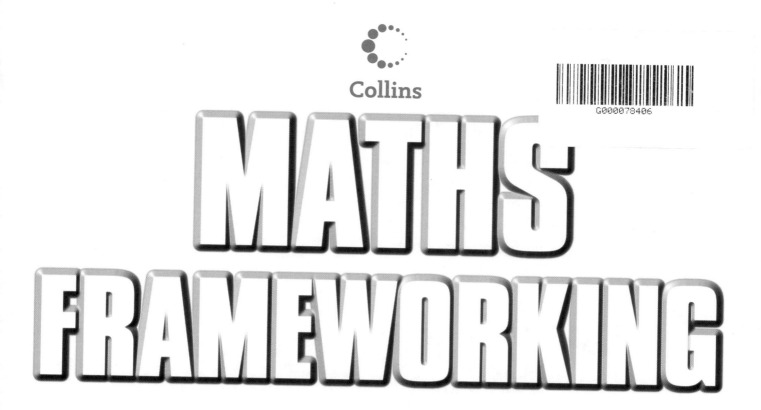

MATHS FRAMEWORKING

Complete success for Mathematics at KS3

YEAR 9

WORKBOOK

Contents

CHAPTER 1

Algebra **1** and **2**

Exercise 1A   Mental addition and subtraction

This exercise will give you practice in

- adding and subtracting whole numbers (integers) using mental methods

1 Work out each of the following additions.

a   7 + 13   _20_   b   11 + 19   _30_   c   23 + 60   _83_

d   44 + 36   _80_   e   55 + 37   _92_   f   138 + 41   _179_

g   216 + 134   _350_   h   350 + 260   _610_   i   259 + 113   _372_

2 Add together the following numbers.

a   73 and 37   _110_   b   35 and 36   _71_

c   –2 and 5   _3_   d   –7 and 3   _–4_

e   37, 38 and 39   _114_   f   18, 19, 20 and 21   _98_

3 Work out each of the following subtractions.

a   19 – 7   _____   b   18 – 6   _____   c   30 – 14   _____

d   84 – 29   _____   e   100 – 16   _____   f   240 – 45   _____

g   152 – 41   _____   h   136 – 78   _____   i   1000 – 866   _____

4 Fill in the missing number in each of the following calculations.

a   ☐ + 7 = 18   b   24 – ☐ = 15   c   13 + ☐ = 37

d   ☐ – 18 = 9   e   28 – ☐ = 9   f   17 + ☐ = 54

5 Look at the numbers in the box then answer the questions.

a   Which two numbers added together make 220? _____

b   Which two numbers have a sum of 110? _____

c   Which two numbers have a difference of 90? _____

40	70
270	30
130	50
230	90

Exercise 1B   Mental multiplication

This exercise will give you practice in

- multiplying whole numbers (integers) using mental methods

1 Complete the following multiplication tables.

a

×	4	3	7
2			
5			35
10			

b

×	7	8	9
4			
6	42		
7			

2 Work out each of the following multiplications.

a 3×4 _____

b 7×5 _____

c 4×6 _____

d 8×3 _____

e 6×9 _____

f 7×8 _____

3 Work out each of the following multiplications.

a $2 \times 3 \times 4$ _____

b $5 \times 2 \times 3$ _____

c $3 \times 2 \times 7$ _____

d $8 \times 5 \times 2$ _____

e $4 \times 4 \times 5$ _____

f $9 \times 9 \times 2$ _____

4 Work out each of the following multiplications.

a 30×7 _____

b 6×40 _____

c 50×7 _____

d 8×90 _____

e 40×8 _____

f 7×70 _____

5 Work out each of the following multiplications mentally. You may make jottings on rough paper if needed.

a 14×2 _____

b 2×19 _____

c 2×23 _____

d 27×2 _____

e 13×3 _____

f 3×21 _____

g 3×17 _____

h 25×3 _____

i 34×3 _____

j 4×12 _____

k 4×19 _____

l 23×4 _____

6 Work out how many:

   a eggs there are in seven boxes.

      _____

   b fish fingers there are in five packets.

   c eggs there are in 25 boxes.

   d chunks of chocolate there are in 40 bars.

   e chunks of chocolate there are in 11 bars.

   f fish fingers there are in 20 packets.

Exercise 1C   Sequences

This exercise will give you practice in

- working out the next terms in a sequence using the term–to–term rule
- finding the term–to–term rule for a given sequence

1 The first term in a sequence is given. Use the term–to–term rule to work out the next five terms in the sequence.

   a The rule is **add 4**.

21					

   b The rule is **add 7**.

−10					

   c The rule is **subtract 6**.

40					

   d The rule is **add 13**.

3					

   e The rule is **subtract 15**.

70					

f The rule is **multiply by 3**.

3					

g The rule is **multiply by 3 then add 1**.

1					

h The rule is **multiply by 2 then add 2**.

1					

i The rule is **multiply by 3 then subtract 4**.

3					

2 Work out the term–to–term rule that has been used to generate each sequence.

a 25, 28, 31, 34, 37, 40, ...   The rule is _____

b 99, 94, 89, 84, 79, 74, ...   The rule is _____

c 0, –2, –4, –6, –8, –10, ...   The rule is _____

d 1, 2, 4, 8, 16, 32, ...   The rule is _____

e –14, –5, 4, 13, 22, 31, ...   The rule is _____

f 29, 22, 15, 8, 1, –6, ...   The rule is _____

g 3, 14, 25, 36, 47, 58, 69, ...   The rule is _____

h 525, 505, 485, 465, 445, ...   The rule is _____

i 2, 6, 18, 54, 162, 486, ...   The rule is _____

j 1, 10, 100, 1000, 10 000, ...   The rule is _____

k 160, 80, 40, 20, 10, 5, ...   The rule is _____

3 Work out the missing terms in each of the following sequences.

a ☐ , ☐ , 15, 19, 23, ☐ , 31   **b** ☐ , 30, 37, 44, ☐ , 58, ☐

c ☐ , 150, 130, 110, ☐ , ☐ , 50   **d** ☐ , 18, 36, 72, 144, ☐

Exercise 1D   Function machines

This exercise will give you practice in
- finding inputs and outputs of functions
- working out the function which has been used

1 Fill in the outputs of each function machine.

a → | Add 9 | →

Input	Output
7 →	_____
13 →	_____
36 →	_____
103 →	_____

b → | Subtract 8 | →

Input	Output
10 →	_____
32 →	_____
8 →	_____
122 →	_____

c → | Multiply by 6 | →

Input	Output
7 →	_____
4 →	_____
13 →	_____
100 →	_____

d → | Subtract 3 | → | Multiply by 3 | →

Input		Output
4 →	_____ →	_____
5 →	_____ →	_____
8 →	_____ →	_____
15 →	_____ →	_____

2 Fill in the inputs of each function machine.

a → | Add 6 | →

Input	Output
_____ →	10
_____ →	16
_____ →	23
_____ →	50

b → | Subtract 8 | →

Input	Output
_____ →	2
_____ →	5
_____ →	10
_____ →	32

c → | Multiply by 4 | →

Input	Output
_____ →	8
_____ →	16
_____ →	32
_____ →	40

d → | Multiply by 9 | →

Input	Output
_____ →	27
_____ →	81
_____ →	45
_____ →	90

3 Fill in the missing function for each of the following function machines.

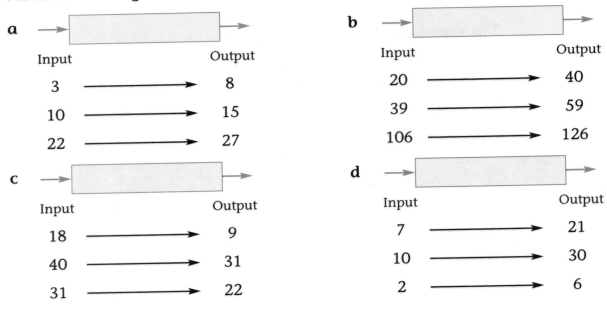

a

Input   Output

3 ——→ 8

10 ——→ 15

22 ——→ 27

b

Input   Output

20 ——→ 40

39 ——→ 59

106 ——→ 126

c

Input   Output

18 ——→ 9

40 ——→ 31

31 ——→ 22

d

Input   Output

7 ——→ 21

10 ——→ 30

2 ——→ 6

Exercise 1E   Terms and expressions

This exercise will give you practice in

- using letters for numbers
- using letters in rules and functions

1 Match each of the word statements to an expression. The letter *n* stands for 'a number'. The first one has been done for you.

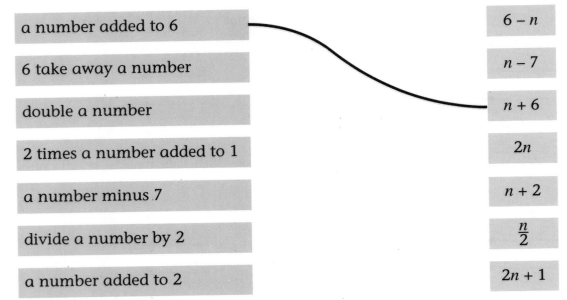

a number added to 6

6 take away a number

double a number

2 times a number added to 1

a number minus 7

divide a number by 2

a number added to 2

$6 - n$

$n - 7$

$n + 6$

$2n$

$n + 2$

$\dfrac{n}{2}$

$2n + 1$

2 In this question the letters a, b and c represent three numbers.

Write down the value of each expression for the values of a, b and c given below.

$a = 3$ $b = 7$ $c = 4$

a $a + 5$ _____ **b** $10 - c$ _____ **c** $b + 3$ _____ **d** $b - 1$ _____

e $c + 12$ _____ **f** $2c$ _____ **g** $2b$ _____ **h** $3a$ _____

3 Fill in the missing outputs for each function machine below.

a → $n + 6$ →

Input   Output

2 ——→ _____

5 ——→ _____

10 ——→ _____

34 ——→ _____

b → $n - 3$ →

Input   Output

3 ——→ _____

7 ——→ _____

15 ——→ _____

28 ——→ _____

c → $4n$ →

Input   Output

2 ——→ _____

5 ——→ _____

10 ——→ _____

25 ——→ _____

d → $7n$ →

Input   Output

1 ——→ _____

2 ——→ _____

5 ——→ _____

10 ——→ _____

e → $\dfrac{n}{2}$ →

Input   Output

4 ——→ _____

10 ——→ _____

20 ——→ _____

44 ——→ _____

f → $3n + 1$ →

Input   Output

1 ——→ _____

2 ——→ _____

4 ——→ _____

9 ——→ _____

Exercise 1F   Graphs from functions

This exercise will give you practice in

● drawing a graph from a simple equation

For each question you should:

a   complete the table of values by working out the value of y for each value of x;

b   complete the coordinates of the points for the graph;

c   draw the axes on graph paper, plot the points and draw a straight line through them.

1   The equation is $y = x + 2$.

x	0	2	3	5
y				

(0, ————)

(2, ————)

(3, ————)

(5, ————)

2   The equation is $y = 5 - x$.

x	0	1	3	5
y				

(0, ————)

(1, ————)

(3, ————)

(5, ————)

3   The equation is $y = 3x$.

x	0	1	2	3
y				

(0, ————)

(1, ————)

(2, ————)

(3, ————)

4   The equation is $y = 2x + 3$.

x	0	1	2	4
y				

(0, ————)

(1, ————)

(2, ————)

(4, ————)

5   The equation is $y = 3x - 4$.

x	1	2	3	4	5
y					

(1, ————)

(2, ————)

(3, ————)

(4, ————)

(5, ————)

Exercise 2A Rounding

This exercise will give you practice in

○ rounding integers to the nearest 10, 100 and 1000
○ rounding decimal numbers to the nearest unit and one or two decimal places

1 Round each of these numbers to the nearest 10.

a 32 _____   b 47 _____   c 94 _____

d 85 _____   e 143 _____   f 176 _____

g 309 _____   h 264 _____   i 897 _____

2 Round each of these numbers to the nearest 100.

a 374 _____   b 830 _____   c 108 _____

d 451 _____   e 1326 _____   f 2407 _____

g 3883 _____   h 5210 _____   i 3892 _____

3 Round each house price to the nearest £1000.

a £123 400   b £175 300   c £188 700   d £204 900

£_____   £_____   £_____   £_____

4 Round each of these decimal numbers to the nearest whole number.

a 3.7 _____   b 6.2 _____   c 9.4 _____

d 8.5 _____   e 14.8 _____   f 36.4 _____

g 6.71 _____   h 4.39 _____   i 6.54 _____

5 Look at the position of the numbers above the arrows. Round each of these numbers to one decimal place.

a   5.67 rounded to one decimal place is _____

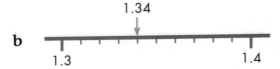

b   1.34 rounded to one decimal place is _____

6 Round each of these numbers to one decimal place.

a   4.63 _____   b   9.75 _____   c   3.28 _____

d   6.19 _____   e   14.34 _____   f   0.53 _____

7 Round each of these numbers to two decimal places.

a   2.357 _____   b   4.218 _____   c   0.874 _____

d   9.855 _____   e   16.263 _____   f   8.859 _____

Exercise 2B   Ordering decimals

This exercise will give you practice in
- comparing two decimal numbers
- putting decimal numbers in order of size

1 Write down the numbers that the arrows are pointing to.

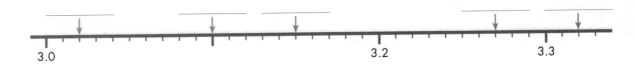

2 Circle the larger number in each pair of decimal numbers below.

a   0.6   0.7   b   4.3   4.4   c   12.6   12.5

d   10.9   10.0   e   3.4   4.3   f   7.7   8.7

g   9.35   9.38   h   4.75   4.71   i   4.63   4.43

j   0.71   0.07   k   0.3   0.03   l   0.09   0.9

m   1.6   1.65   n   2.47   2.4   p   8.7   8.67

3 Order each group of decimal fractions in order of size, starting with the smallest.

a   4.3   4.7   3.4   7.4   _____ , _____ , _____ , _____

b   0.6   6.0   6.6   1.6   _____ , _____ , _____ , _____

c   19.3   13.3   13.9   11.3   _____ , _____ , _____ , _____

d   63.4   34.6   46.4   34.4   _____ , _____ , _____ , _____

4 Put these amounts of money in order of size, starting with the smallest.

a   £1.08   £1.80   £0.88   £8.81   _____ , _____ , _____ , _____

b   £3.41   £3.14   £3.61   £4.13   _____ , _____ , _____ , _____

c   £61.42   £60.24   £64.04   £60.40   _____ , _____ , _____ , _____

d   £0.85   £0.87   £0.78   £0.58   _____ , _____ , _____ , _____

Exercise 2C   Fractions and decimals

This exercise will give you practice in

- changing proper fractions and mixed numbers to decimal fractions
- changing decimal fractions to proper fractions or mixed numbers

1 Write down how much of each shape is shaded as a proper fraction and a decimal fraction.

a

fraction __1/2__

decimal __0.5__

b

fraction __1/4__

decimal __0.25__

c

fraction __3/4__

decimal __0.75__

d

fraction __1/10__

decimal __0.1__

e

fraction __1/100__

decimal __0.01__

f

fraction __1/5__

decimal __0.2__

2 Write down each of these values as a decimal fraction. The first one has been done for you.

a $\frac{1}{10}$ ___0.1___

b $\frac{3}{10}$ _____

c $\frac{7}{10}$ _____

d $\frac{1}{100}$ _____

e $\frac{3}{100}$ _____

f $\frac{19}{100}$ _____

g $\frac{43}{100}$ _____

h $1\frac{9}{10}$ _____

i $2\frac{43}{100}$ _____

3 Write each of these values as a proper fraction or mixed number.

a 0.1 _____

b 0.3 _____

c 0.9 _____

d 0.01 _____

e 0.07 _____

f 0.11 _____

g 2.7 _____

h 1.13 _____

4 Fill in the missing numbers to complete the equivalences below.

a $0.5 = \dfrac{}{2} = \dfrac{}{10}$

b $0.25 = \dfrac{}{4} = \dfrac{}{100}$

c $0.75 = \dfrac{}{4} = \dfrac{}{100}$

d $0.2 = \dfrac{}{5} = \dfrac{}{10}$

e $0.6 = \dfrac{}{5} = \dfrac{}{10}$

Exercise 2D Adding and subtracting fractions

This exercise will give you practice in

- changing fractions so that they have the same denominator
- adding and subtracting fractions

1 Add each of the following.

a $\dfrac{3}{7} + \dfrac{1}{7} = \dfrac{}{7}$

b $\dfrac{3}{11} + \dfrac{2}{11} = \dfrac{}{11}$

c $\dfrac{4}{9} + \dfrac{1}{9} = \dfrac{}{}$

d $\dfrac{8}{13} + \dfrac{2}{13} = \dfrac{}{}$

e $\dfrac{1}{6} + \dfrac{1}{6} = \dfrac{}{6} = \dfrac{}{}$

f $\dfrac{1}{10} + \dfrac{7}{10} = \dfrac{}{10} = \dfrac{}{}$

2 Subtract each of the following.

a $\dfrac{7}{9} - \dfrac{2}{9} = \dfrac{}{9}$

b $\dfrac{4}{5} - \dfrac{1}{5} = \dfrac{}{5}$

c $\dfrac{8}{9} - \dfrac{4}{9} = \dfrac{}{}$

d $\dfrac{7}{11} - \dfrac{4}{11} = \dfrac{\quad}{\quad}$

e $\dfrac{3}{4} - \dfrac{1}{4} = \dfrac{\quad}{4} = \dfrac{\quad}{\quad}$

f $\dfrac{7}{8} - \dfrac{3}{8} = \dfrac{\quad}{8} = \dfrac{\quad}{\quad}$

3 Fill in the gaps to add the following fractions. Give your answer in its simplest form.

a $\dfrac{2}{3} + \dfrac{1}{6} = \dfrac{\quad}{6} + \dfrac{1}{6} = \dfrac{\quad}{6}$

b $\dfrac{7}{10} + \dfrac{1}{5} = \dfrac{7}{10} + \dfrac{\quad}{10} = \dfrac{\quad}{10}$

c $\dfrac{2}{5} + \dfrac{3}{10} = \dfrac{\quad}{\quad} + \dfrac{\quad}{\quad} = \dfrac{\quad}{\quad}$

d $\dfrac{1}{4} + \dfrac{1}{3} = \dfrac{\quad}{12} + \dfrac{\quad}{12} = \dfrac{\quad}{12}$

e $\dfrac{2}{5} + \dfrac{1}{2} = \dfrac{\quad}{10} + \dfrac{\quad}{10} = \dfrac{\quad}{10}$

f $\dfrac{2}{5} + \dfrac{1}{3} = \dfrac{\quad}{\quad} + \dfrac{\quad}{\quad} = \dfrac{\quad}{\quad}$

4 Fill in the gaps to subtract the following fractions. Give your answer in its simplest form.

a $\dfrac{5}{6} - \dfrac{1}{3} = \dfrac{5}{6} - \dfrac{\quad}{6} = \dfrac{\quad}{6} = \dfrac{\quad}{\quad}$

b $\dfrac{4}{5} - \dfrac{3}{10} = \dfrac{\quad}{10} - \dfrac{3}{10} = \dfrac{\quad}{10} = \dfrac{\quad}{\quad}$

c $\dfrac{2}{3} - \dfrac{1}{6} = \dfrac{\quad}{\quad} - \dfrac{\quad}{\quad} = \dfrac{\quad}{\quad} = \dfrac{\quad}{\quad}$

d $\dfrac{9}{10} - \dfrac{2}{5} = \dfrac{\quad}{\quad} - \dfrac{\quad}{\quad} = \dfrac{\quad}{\quad} = \dfrac{\quad}{\quad}$

e $\dfrac{3}{4} - \dfrac{1}{3} = \dfrac{\quad}{12} - \dfrac{\quad}{12} = \dfrac{\quad}{12}$

f $\dfrac{1}{2} - \dfrac{2}{5} = \dfrac{\quad}{\quad} - \dfrac{\quad}{\quad} = \dfrac{\quad}{\quad}$

Exercise 2E Multiplying and dividing with fractions

This exercise will give you practice in

- multiplying and dividing integers by fractions
- calculating fractions of quantities

1 Write down and work out the equivalent division calculation to each of the following multiplication calculations. Parts **a** to **d** have been started for you.

a $4 \times \dfrac{1}{2} = 4 \div 2 = \underline{\qquad}$

b $9 \times \dfrac{1}{3} = 9 \div 3 = \underline{\qquad}$

c $\dfrac{1}{2} \times 10 = 10 \div 2 = \underline{\qquad}$

d $\dfrac{1}{4} \times 16 = 16 \div 4 = \underline{\qquad}$

e $8 \times \dfrac{1}{4} = \underline{\qquad} = \underline{\qquad}$

f $12 \times \dfrac{1}{2} = \underline{\qquad} = \underline{\qquad}$

g $\frac{1}{5} \times 20 = $ _____ = _____

h $24 \times \frac{1}{4} = $ _____ = _____

i $\frac{1}{5} \times 15 = $ _____ = _____

j $\frac{1}{6} \times 18 = $ _____ = _____

2 Write down the answers to each of the following.

a $\frac{1}{3}$ of £9 = 9 ÷ 3 = £_____

b $\frac{1}{4}$ of 24 kg = 24 ÷ 4 = _____ kg

c $\frac{1}{5}$ of £30 = _____ ÷ _____ = _____

d $\frac{1}{2}$ of 28 kg = _____ ÷ _____ = _____

3 Find the quantities on the left by completing the calculations on the right.

a $\frac{2}{3}$ of 12

$\frac{1}{3}$ of 12 = 12 ÷ 3 = _____

$\frac{2}{3}$ of 12 = 2 × _____ = _____

b $\frac{3}{4}$ of 8

$\frac{1}{4}$ of 8 = 8 ÷ 4 = _____

$\frac{3}{4}$ of 8 = 3 × _____ = _____

c $\frac{4}{5}$ of 20

$\frac{1}{5}$ of 20 = _____ = _____

$\frac{4}{5}$ of 20 = _____ = _____

d $\frac{3}{7}$ of 21

$\frac{1}{7}$ of 21 = _____ = _____

$\frac{3}{7}$ of 21 = _____ = _____

4 Write down and work out the equivalent multiplication calculation to each of the following division calculations. Parts **a** to **d** have been started for you.

a $5 \div \frac{1}{2} = 5 \times 2 = $ _____

b $4 \div \frac{1}{3} = 4 \times 3 = $ _____

c $2 \div \frac{1}{5} = 2 \times 5 = $ _____

d $7 \div \frac{1}{4} = 7 \times 4 = $ _____

e $3 \div \frac{1}{2} = $ _____ = _____

f $5 \div \frac{1}{6} = $ _____ = _____

g $7 \div \frac{1}{3} = $ _____ = _____

h $9 \div \frac{1}{6} = $ _____ = _____

Exercise 2F   Percentages

This exercise will give you practice in
- writing percentages as a number of hundredths
- finding percentages of whole numbers

1 Write the equivalent fraction (hundredths) for each of these percentages.

a $15\% = \dfrac{}{100}$

b $34\% = \dfrac{}{100}$

c $93\% = \dfrac{}{100}$

d $7\% = \dfrac{}{100}$

e $20\% = \dfrac{}{100}$

f $3\% = \dfrac{}{100}$

2 Calculate each of the percentages below by first finding 1% of the given quantity and then multiplying.

a 1% of £300 = $\frac{1}{100}$ × £300 = £300 ÷ 100 = £3

Find **i**   2% of £300 = 2 × £3 = £ _6_

   ii 7% of £300 = 7 × £3 = £ _21_

   iii 10% of £300 = 10 × £3 = £ _30_

   iv 20% of £300 = _2_ × £3 = £ _6_

   v 25% of £300 = _2.5_ × £3 = £ _7.50_

   vi 80% of £300 = _8_ × £3 = £ _24_

b 1% of 700 kg = $\frac{1}{100}$ × 700 = 700 ÷ 100 = _____ kg

Find **i**   3% of 700 kg = 3 × _____ kg = _____ kg

   ii 6% of 700 kg = 6 × _____ kg = _____ kg

   iii 30% of 700 kg = _____ × _____ kg = _____ kg

   iv 35% of 700 kg = _____ × _____ kg = _____ kg

c 1% of 2000 m = $\frac{1}{100}$ × 2000 = _____ = _____ m

Find **i**   3% of 2000 m = 3 × _____ m = _____ m

   ii 6% of 2000 m = 6 × _____ m = _____ m

   iii 25% of 2000 m = _____ × _____ m = _____ m

   iv 40% of 2000 m = _____ × _____ m = _____ m

3 Use a calculator to work out each of the following quantities. Write down your calculation.

a   35% of 60 = 35 ÷ 100 × 60 = _____

b   24% of 120 = 24 ÷ 100 × 120 = _____

c   68% of 80 = _____ = _____

d   13% of 50 = _____ = _____

e   8% of 124 = _____ = _____

f   73% of 52 = _____ = _____

Exercise 2G   Reducing ratios

This exercise will give you practice in
- writing a ratio in its simplest form

1 Draw a line between the equivalent ratios.

6 : 2      1 : 1

2 : 2   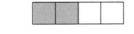   1 : 2

2 : 4   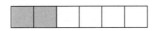   2 : 1

4 : 2      1 : 3

2 : 6   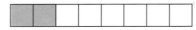   3 : 1

2 Write each ratio in its simplest form.

a   3 : 6   b   10 : 5   c   6 : 6   d   9 : 3

_____ : _____   _____ : _____   _____ : _____   _____ : _____

e   10 : 15   f   6 : 2   g   10 : 2   h   9 : 21

_____ : _____   _____ : _____   _____ : _____   _____ : _____

i   4 : 16   j   10 : 35   k   16 : 24   l   21 : 35

_____ : _____   _____ : _____   _____ : _____   _____ : _____

3 There are 10 girls and 15 boys in class 9B.

Write the ratio of **girls to boys** then rewrite the ratio in its simplest form.

_____ : _____

_____ : _____

4 There are 12 boys and 15 girls in class 9C.

Write the ratio of **boys to girls** then rewrite the ratio in its simplest form.

_____ : _____

_____ : _____

5 There are 18 girls and 12 boys in class 9A.

Write the ratio of **girls to boys** then rewrite the ratio in its simplest form.

_____ : _____

_____ : _____

6 There are 28 students in class 9D. Half of them are girls. Write the ratio of **girls to boys** then rewrite the ratio in its simplest form.

_____ : _____

_____ : _____

7 There are 30 students in class 9E. 14 of them are boys. Write the ratio of **boys to girls** then rewrite the ratio in its simplest form.

_____ : _____

_____ : _____

Exercise 2H   Solving problems using ratios

This exercise will give you practice in

o solving problems using ratios by sharing and multiplying an amount in a given ratio

1 Bethany is making patterns with black and white tiles.

In each pattern she uses one black tile for every three white tiles.

a   Write the ratio of black to white tiles. __1__ : __3__

b   Bethany makes a pattern with four black tiles.

How many white tiles does she use? __12__

c   Bethany makes a pattern with 10 black tiles.

How many white tiles does she use? __30__

d   Bethany makes a pattern with nine white tiles.

How many black tiles does she use? _____

e   Bethany makes a pattern with 18 white tiles.

How many black tiles does she use? _____

2 Michael is making light green paint by mixing blue and yellow paint.

He uses three pots of yellow paint for every two pots of blue.

a   Write the ratio of yellow to blue paint. _____ : _____

b   How many pots of blue paint will he need to mix with

six pots of yellow paint? _____

c   How many pots of blue paint will he need to mix with

12 pots of yellow paint? _____

d   How many pots of yellow paint will he need to mix with

four pots of blue paint? _____

e   How many pots of yellow paint will he need to mix with

10 pots of blue paint? _____

3 Share each amount in the given ratio.

a   £10 in the ratio 1 : 1   £_____ : £_____

b   £9 in the ratio 1 : 2   £_____ : £_____

c   12 m in the ratio 2 : 1   _____ m : _____ m

d   £40 in the ratio 3 : 1   £_____ : £_____

e $20 in the ratio 2 : 3 $_____ : $_____

f   42 kg in the ratio 2 : 5   _____ kg : _____ kg

g   250 ml in the ratio 4 : 1   _____ ml : _____ ml

h   £240 in the ratio 1 : 5   £_____ : £_____

4 In a box of 40 chocolates, the ratio of milk chocolates to plain chocolates is 3 : 2.

How many milk chocolates are there? _____

How many plain chocolates are there? _____

CHAPTER 3   Algebra 3

Exercise 3A   Finding unknown numbers

This exercise will give you practice in

- finding missing numbers in additions, subtractions, multiplications and divisions

1 Fill in the boxes to make each addition or subtraction calculation correct.

   a $7 + \boxed{} = 15$ **b** $11 + \boxed{} = 24$ **c** $8 - \boxed{} = 6$

   d $\boxed{} - 9 = 8$ **e** $\boxed{} + 14 = 26$ **f** $38 - \boxed{} = 21$

   g $\boxed{} + 16 = 43$ **h** $\boxed{} - 15 = 9$ **i** $\boxed{} - 25 = 13$

2 Fill in the boxes to make each multiplication or division calculation correct.

   a $\boxed{} \times 6 = 30$ **b** $\boxed{} \times 9 = 36$ **c** $9 \times \boxed{} = 81$

   d $7 \times \boxed{} = 42$ **e** $3 \times \boxed{} = 21$ **f** $20 \div \boxed{} = 4$

   g $24 \div \boxed{} = 6$ **h** $48 \div \boxed{} = 6$ **i** $\boxed{} \times 10 = 70$

3 Write down two pairs of numbers that could go in the empty boxes to make each of these calculations correct.

   a $\boxed{} + \boxed{} = 15$ $\boxed{} + \boxed{} = 15$

   b $\boxed{} - \boxed{} = 9$ $\boxed{} - \boxed{} = 9$

   c $\boxed{} \times \boxed{} = 28$ $\boxed{} \times \boxed{} = 28$

   d $\boxed{} \div \boxed{} = 7$ $\boxed{} \div \boxed{} = 7$

4 Fill in the boxes to make each of these calculations correct.

   a $\boxed{} \times 3 + 7 = 13$ **b** $4 \times \boxed{} - 1 = 19$ **c** $\boxed{} \times 5 + 3 = 28$

   d $7 \times \boxed{} + 3 = 17$ **e** $17 - 3 \times \boxed{} = 8$ **f** $15 + 3 \times \boxed{} = 15$

Exercise 3B Calculating using rules

This exercise will give you practice in

- calculating answers to problems using rules

1 The distance travelled along a motorway can be calculated by the rule:

Distance in miles = number of hours driving × 70

How far would you travel on a motorway in

a 2 hours? _____

b 5 hours? _____

2 Mr and Mrs George decide to give their three children monthly pocket money.
They use the rule:

Pocket money in pounds = child's age + 4

Julianna is 7, Rachel is 12 and Liselle is 14.

How much will they each receive?

a Julianna _____

b Rachel _____

c Liselle _____

3 A DJ charges for discos using the rule:

Charge = £70 plus £40 for every hour past midnight

How much would the DJ charge for the following discos?

a Finish at 1:00 am _____

b Finish at 3:00 am _____

4 Jade makes and sells bead bracelets. She uses the rule:

number of beads = number of bracelets × 12

to work out how many beads she will need for each order of bracelets.

a How many beads will she need for an order of

i 10 bracelets? _____

ii 30 bracelets? _____

iii 100 bracelets? _____

b Jade has 60 spare beads left over.

How many extra bracelets can she make? _____

5 Simon runs laps around a running track. He uses the rule:

number of miles = number of laps ÷ 4

to work out how many miles he has run around the track.

a How many miles did he run if he completed

i 8 laps? _____

ii 20 laps? _____

iii 32 laps? _____

b Simon wants to run 3 miles around the track. How many laps should he complete?

_____

6 A florist uses the rule:

total cost = cost of bouquet + £4

to work out how much to charge a customer for delivery of a bouquet of flowers.

a How much would the total cost be, including delivery, for

i a bouquet costing £10? _____

ii a bouquet costing £17? _____

iii a bouquet costing £29? _____

b A customer was charged £26 in total. How much was the bouquet worth?

_____

Exercise 3C Simplifying terms and expressions

This exercise will give you practice in
- simplifying algebraic expressions
- collecting like terms
- substituting positive integers into simple linear expressions

1 Simplify each of these expressions.

a $n + n + n$ _____ **b** $a + a + a + a$ _____

c $p + p$ _____ **d** $q + q + q + q + q$ _____

e $e + e + e + e$ _____ **f** $t + t + t$ _____

g $b + b + b + b + b + b$ _____

h $c + c$ _____

i $x + x + x + x + x + x + x$ _____

j $y + y + y$ _____

2 Simplify each of these expressions.

a $3a + 2a$ _____

b $7c + 5c$ _____

c $8m + 9m$ _____

d $5d - 3d$ _____

e $q + 3q$ _____

f $10a - 5a$ _____

g $7c - 4c$ _____

h $3a - a$ _____

i $2c + 3c + c$ _____

3 Simplify each of these expressions.

a $c + c + c + d + d$ _____

b $p + p + q + q + q + q$ _____

c $j + k + k + k$ _____

d $s + s + s + s + t + t + t$ _____

e $a + b + b + a + a$ _____

f $g + h + g + h + g + h$ _____

g $x + x + y + y + y + y + x$ _____

h $m + n + n + n + n + m$ _____

4 Write down the values of each expression for the three values of n given.

a $n + 1$ $n = 2$ _____ $n = 5$ _____ $n = 11$ _____

b $n + 7$ $n = 3$ _____ $n = 6$ _____ $n = 7$ _____

c $n - 3$ $n = 10$ _____ $n = 5$ _____ $n = 20$ _____

d $n - 4$ $n = 20$ _____ $n = 50$ _____ $n = 100$ _____

e $3n$ $n = 3$ _____ $n = 4$ _____ $n = 7$ _____

f $10n$ $n = 2$ _____ $n = 5$ _____ $n = 8$ _____

Exercise 3D   Formulae

This exercise will give you practice in

- using a formula

1 A café orders eggs in boxes of six. The formula for working out the total number of eggs delivered is:

$E = 6N$ **where**   E = number of eggs
N = number of boxes

REMEMBER!
6N means $6 \times N$

Use the formula to work out the number of eggs if the café orders a   6 boxes. _____

b   10 boxes. _____

c   30 boxes. _____

2 Jake is 7 years younger than his brother, Paul. The formula for working out Jake's age is:

$J = P – 7$ **where**   **J = Jake's age**
P = Paul's age

Use the formula to work out what Jake's age will be when Paul is

a   20 years old. _____

b   34 years old. _____

c   51 years old. _____

3 A taxi driver uses this formula to work out the cost of a taxi fare:

$F = £2m + £1$ **where**   **F = fare**
m = number of miles travelled

REMEMBER!
2m means 2 × m

Use the formula to work out the fare for a journey of

a   2 miles. _____

b   5 miles. _____

c   11 miles. _____

4 The formula for working out the total number of marks in a maths exam is:

$T = A + B$ **where**   **T = total number of marks**
A = marks in paper 1
B = marks in paper 2

Use the formula to work out the total marks for a student who scored

a   13 on paper 1 and 23 on paper 2. _____

b   24 on paper 1 and 18 on paper 2. _____

c   19 on paper 1 and 17 on paper 2. _____

5 Work out the value of **T** where $x = 15$ and $y = 7$ using the formula:

$T = x – y$ T = _____ – _____

                  T = _____

6 Work out the value of **M** where $a = 3$ and $b = 9$ using the formula:

$\mathbf{M} = \textbf{\textit{ab}}$ $M = \underline{\hspace{1.5cm}} \times \underline{\hspace{1.5cm}}$

$M = \underline{\hspace{1.5cm}}$

7 Work out the value of **A** where $d = 7$ using the formula:

$\mathbf{A} = \textbf{3}\textbf{\textit{d}} + \textbf{2}$ $A = 3 \times \underline{\hspace{1.5cm}} + 2$

$A = \underline{\hspace{1.5cm}} + 2$

$A = \underline{\hspace{1.5cm}}$

8 Work out the value of **P** where $a = 3$ and $b = 4$ using the formula:

$\mathbf{P} = \textbf{2}\textbf{\textit{a}} + \textbf{2}\textbf{\textit{b}}$ $P = 2 \times \underline{\hspace{1.5cm}} + 2 \times \underline{\hspace{1.5cm}}$

$P = \underline{\hspace{1.5cm}} + \underline{\hspace{1.5cm}}$

$P = \underline{\hspace{1.5cm}}$

Exercise 3E Equations

This exercise will give you practice in

o setting out and starting to solve simple equations

1 Fill in the spaces to solve each equation.

a $x + 4 = 7$

Subtract $\underline{\hspace{1cm}}$ from both sides

$x + 4 \underline{\hspace{1cm}} = 7 \underline{\hspace{1cm}}$

$x = \underline{\hspace{1cm}}$

b $x + 9 = 13$

Subtract $\underline{\hspace{1cm}}$ from both sides

$x + 9 \underline{\hspace{1cm}} = 13 \underline{\hspace{1cm}}$

$x = \underline{\hspace{1cm}}$

c $x + 7 = 15$

$\underline{\hspace{3cm}}$ from both sides

$\underline{\hspace{2cm}} = \underline{\hspace{2cm}}$

$x = \underline{\hspace{1cm}}$

d $x + 5 = 20$

$\underline{\hspace{3cm}}$ from both sides

$\underline{\hspace{2cm}} = \underline{\hspace{2cm}}$

$x = \underline{\hspace{1cm}}$

e $x + 1 = 9$

f $x + 8 = 18$

g $x - 5 = 3$

Add _____ to both sides

$x - 5$ _____ $= 3$ _____

$x =$ _____

h $x - 2 = 9$

Add _____ to both sides

$x - 2$ _____ $= 9$ _____

$x =$ _____

i $x - 3 = 11$

_____ to both sides

_____ $=$ _____

$x =$ _____

j $x - 7 = 13$

_____ to both sides

_____ $=$ _____

$x =$ _____

k $x - 8 = 10$

_____

_____

_____

l $x - 4 = 18$

_____

_____

_____

2 Fill in the spaces to solve each equation.

a $3x = 12$

Divide both sides by _____

$3x \div$ _____ $= 12 \div$ _____

$x =$ _____

b $5x = 25$

Divide both sides by _____

$5x \div$ _____ $= 25 \div$ _____

$x =$ _____

c $4x = 8$

Divide both sides by _____

$4x \div$ _____ $= 8 \div$ _____

$x =$ _____

d $6x = 30$

Divide both sides by _____

$6x \div$ _____ $= 30 \div$ _____

$x =$ _____

e $3x = 18$

_____

_____ $=$ _____

$x =$ _____

f $5x = 40$

_____

_____ $=$ _____

$x =$ _____

g $7x = 21$

_____

_____ $=$ _____

$x =$ _____

h $4x = 16$

_____

_____ $=$ _____

$x =$ _____

Exercise 4A   Properties of a triangle

This exercise will give you practice in

- recognising properties of different triangles

1 Here is a piece of patterned wallpaper border.

Fill in the blanks to describe the triangles in the pattern.

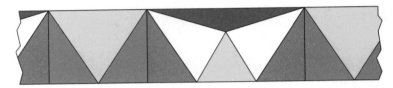

The yellow triangles are _____ triangles. The blue triangle is an _____ triangle. The red and green triangles are _____ triangles.

2 Tick the statements which are true.

A scalene triangle has no equal sides. ☐

An isosceles triangle has three equal sides. ☐

An equilateral triangle has one 90° angle. ☐

An isosceles triangle has two equal sides. ☐

A right-angled triangle has one obtuse angle. ☐

An equilateral triangle has three equal angles. ☐

3 Draw lines of symmetry on those triangles which have reflective symmetry.

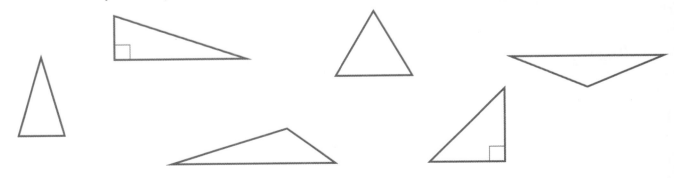

4 Draw four different isosceles triangles on the dotty grids.

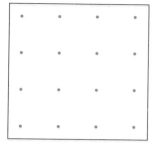 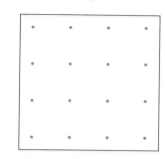 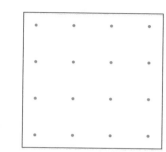 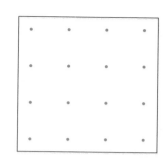

Exercise 4B   Identifying alternate angles

This exercise will give you practice in
- identifying a pair of alternate angles
- working out the size of an alternate angle

1 Tick the box if the diagram shows a pair of alternate angles. Put a cross in the box if it does not.

a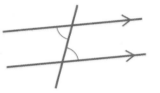

b

c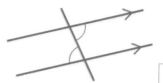

d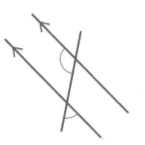

e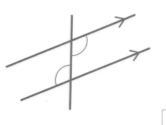

f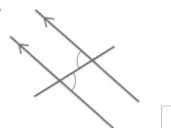

2 Mark the angle which is alternate to the one already marked.

a

b

c

d 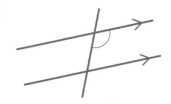 **e** 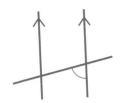 **f**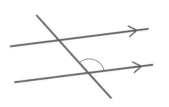

3 Work out the size of the angles marked with letters.

a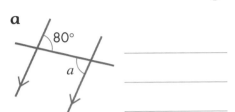

_____

_____

_____

b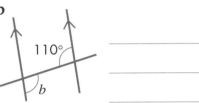

_____

_____

_____

c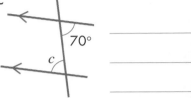

_____

_____

_____

d

_____

_____

_____

e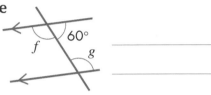

_____

_____

_____

f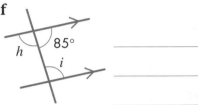

_____

_____

_____

Exercise 4C Corresponding angles

This exercise will give you practice in

- identifying a pair of corresponding angles
- working out the size of a corresponding angle

1 Tick the box if the diagram shows a pair of corresponding angles. Put a cross in the box if it does not.

a 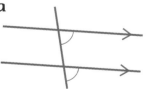 ☐

b 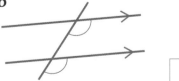 ☐

c  ☐

d  ☐

e  ☐

f  ☐

2 Mark the angle which corresponds to the one already marked.

a

b

c

d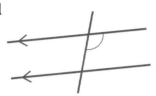

e

f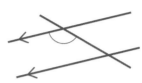

3 Work out the size of the angles marked with letters.

a

_____

_____

b

_____

_____

c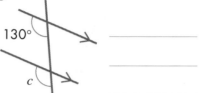

_____

_____

d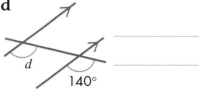

_____

_____

e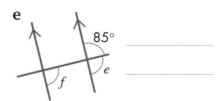

_____

_____

f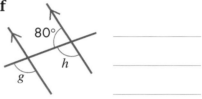

_____

_____

Exercise 4D   Finding unknown angles

This exercise will give you practice in

- working out the size of an unknown angle in a triangle
- working out the size of an unknown angle in a quadrilateral

1 Find the size of the angle marked by a letter in each scalene or right-angled triangle.

a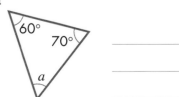

_____

_____

_____

b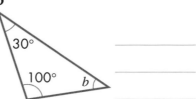

_____

_____

_____

c

_____

_____

d

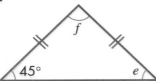

80°
60°

_____

_____

_____

e

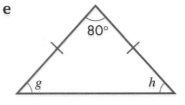

40°
30°

_____

_____

_____

f

50°

_____

_____

_____

---

2 Find the size of the unknown angles in each isosceles or equilateral triangle.

a

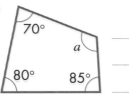

40°
70°   a

_____

_____

_____

b

_____

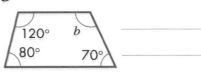

100°
40°   b

_____

_____

c

d
75°   c

_____

_____

_____

d

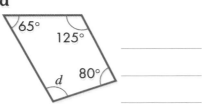

f
45°   e

_____

_____

_____

e

80°
g   h

_____

_____

_____

---

3 Find the size of the angle marked by a letter in each quadrilateral.

a

70°
a
80°   85°

_____

_____

_____

b

120°   b
80°   70°

_____

_____

_____

c

c
140°
80°   85°

_____

_____

_____

d

65°
125°
d   80°

_____

_____

_____

e

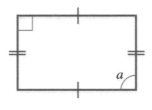

e
130°
110°

_____

_____

_____

f

75°
105°
f
40°

_____

_____

_____

---

4 Find the size of the angle marked _a_ in the quadrilateral below.

a

_____

CHAPTER 5

Handling Data **1**

Exercise 5A Data collection sheets

This exercise will give you practice in
- designing and completing data collection sheets

1 Phil throws a dice 30 times and obtains the following scores.

2	6	1	3	1	3	2	5	1	6	6	1	2	5	1
3	6	5	4	4	1	1	4	6	5	2	5	3	2	5

Copy and complete the survey sheet below.

Score	Tally	Frequency
1		
2		
3		
4		
5		
6		
	Total	

2 Liam has been carrying out a survey to find out how students get to school. As students came in through the gates he listed the method each used. He collected data from 30 students.

car, walk, bus, bus, bus, walk, car, walk, cycle, walk, bus, bus, bus, car, car, walk, walk, walk, bus, bus, bus, walk, bus, walk, cycle, car, walk, car, bus, bus

A more efficient method would have been to use a tally chart. Design a suitable tally chart, with frequency column, and complete it using the data.

2 Neela is collecting data about the number of days that students in her class have been absent this year. Here is her data.

0	3	5	0	19	12	18	6	0	5	1	1	2	5
0	1	28	27	14	1	3	6	5	2	2	8	4	13

Use the data to complete her data collection sheet.

Number of days absent	Tally	Frequency
0–4		
5–9		
10–14		
15–19		
20–24		
25–29		

Exercise 5B   Questionnaires

This exercise will give you practice in
- designing a questionnaire for use in collecting data

1 Here is a questionnaire which will be used to collect data about students' TV viewing habits. Criticise each question.

a Which of the main TV channels do you watch the most?

BBC1 ☐   BBC2 ☐   ITV1 ☐

Channel 4 ☐   Channel 5 ☐   Channel 6 ☐

b What is your favourite type of programme?   Sports ☐   Comedy ☐

c In a typical day, how much TV do you watch?

less than 2 hours ☐   2–4 hours ☐   more than 6 hours ☐

d   How often do you watch films on TV?   Yes ☐   No ☐

_____

_____

2 Give some suitable 'tick box' style answers for each question.

   a   How do you travel to school?

   b   How long does your journey usually take?

   c   Have you ever been late for school?

3 Design a questionnaire which you could use to collect data about what people in your school do during the holidays. Using A4 paper, write **four** questions with 'tick box' style answers.

Exercise 5C   Statistical diagrams

This exercise will give you practice in
- constructing bar charts and bar-line graphs on graph paper

1 Kirsty has carried out a survey to find out which is the most common colour for cars. She has recorded her results in a tally chart.

Colour of car	Tally	Frequency
red	⊥⊦⊦⊤ ⊥⊦⊦⊤ ⊥⊦⊦⊤ ⊥⊦⊦⊤ ⊥⊦⊦⊤ ⊥⊦⊦⊤ ⏐⏐⏐⏐	
blue	⊥⊦⊦⊤ ⏐⏐⏐	
black	⊥⊦⊦⊤ ⊥⊦⊦⊤ ⊥⊦⊦⊤ ⊥⊦⊦⊤ ⊥⊦⊦⊤	
silver	⊥⊦⊦⊤ ⊥⊦⊦⊤	
white	⊥⊦⊦⊤ ⊥⊦⊦⊤ ⊥⊦⊦⊤ ⊥⊦⊦⊤	
other	⊥⊦⊦⊤ ⊥⊦⊦⊤ ⏐⏐	

Complete the frequency values and then use them to draw a **bar chart** on graph paper.

Remember to label your axes, think carefully about the vertical scale and give your bar chart a title.

2 Adam has recorded the number of students who take part in the five different after-school clubs on a Wednesday.

Draw a **bar-line graph** of his results on graph paper.

Activity	Cross-country	Netball	Computers	Orchestra	Yoga
Number of students	15	23	17	28	14

3 The data in the frequency table shows the number of ice creams sold in a newsagent's in the months from April to October.

Month	April	May	June	July	August	September	October
Number of ice creams	100	150	250	260	300	180	70

Use the data to draw a **bar-line graph** on graph paper.

Exercise 5D   Statistics

This exercise will give you practice in
- finding the range, mode, mean and median for a set of raw data

1 For each set of numbers find the mode. Some sets of numbers may have more than one mode or possibly no mode at all.

a   £3, £4, £8, £8, £3, £7, £6, £7, £8   Mode _____

b   50, 51, 54, 52, 50, 51, 52, 52, 56   Mode _____

c   0.6, 0.7, 0.6, 0.6, 0.4, 0.6, 0.7, 0.4, 0.7, 0.7   Mode _____

d   4, $4\frac{1}{2}$, 5, 5, $4\frac{1}{2}$, 6, $6\frac{1}{2}$, 4, 5, $4\frac{1}{2}$, $5\frac{1}{2}$ Mode _____

e   £100, £110, £200, £120, £210, £190   Mode _____

2 Find the median of each set of numbers. Remember to put the numbers in order first, starting with the smallest.

a   6, 7, 10, 4, 9   Median _____

b   38, 40, 59, 43, 48   Median _____

c   16, 17, 13, 13, 16, 14, 18   Median _____

d   6, 5, 6, 7, 8, 3   Median _____

e   6, 8, 4, 3, 10, 15   Median _____

f   18, 19, 11, 19, 11, 14   Median _____

3 Find the mean and range of each set of numbers. Remember, to find the mean you add up all of the numbers then divide this total by the number of values in the list. You may use a calculator.

a   3, 5, 6, 10, 8, 10   Range _____   Mean _____

b   16, 18, 4, 3, 12   Range _____   Mean _____

c   2.4, 2.6, 2.8, 2.9, 2.5   Range _____   Mean _____

d   £5.00, £1.62, £3.36, £4.53, £4.21, £1.08   Range _____   Mean _____

4 Here are the weights of the people taking part in a tug-of-war.

Team A   160 kg, 142 kg, 150 kg, 138 kg, 145 kg
Team B   175 kg, 146 kg, 149 kg, 155 kg, 150 kg

a   Work out the mean weight for each team.

Mean for Team A _____   Mean for Team B _____

b   Which team do you think will win? Give a reason using your answer from part **a**.

Exercise 5E   Pie charts

This exercise will give you practice in

- drawing 10-sector pie charts
- drawing pie charts using angles

1   Complete each table and use it to draw a pie chart. Remember to label your pie chart.

a   The table shows the effort grades for 80 students in Year 9.

Each sector of the chart represents _____ students.

Grade	Number of students	Number of sectors on pie chart
A	8	
B	24	
C	24	
D	16	
E	8	

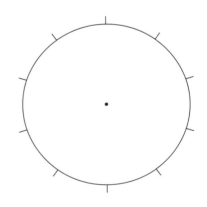

b   The table shows the percentage sales of drinks for a vending machine.
Each sector of the chart represents 10%.

Drink	Percentage	Number of sectors on pie chart
tea	10%	
orange	20%	
coffee	40%	
hot chocolate	25%	
soup	5%	

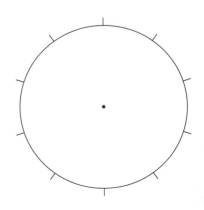

2 Complete each table and use it to draw a pie chart. Remember to label your pie chart.

a The table shows the holiday destinations of 36 people. Each person is represented by _____ °.

Destination	Number of people	Size of sector in °
UK	18	
Europe	9	
USA	6	
Other	3	

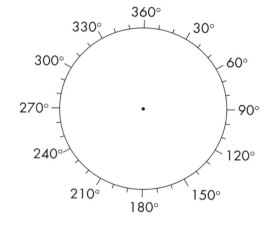

b The table shows the preferred ice-cream flavour of 18 people. Each person is represented by _____ °

Ice-cream flavour	Number of people	Size of sector in °
vanilla	1	
strawberry	2	
mint choc chip	6	
chocolate	9	

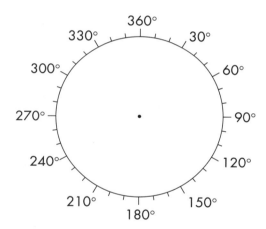

Exercise 5F   Interpreting statistical diagrams

This exercise will give you practice in
- reading information from tables, graphs and diagrams

1 The bar chart on the next page shows what students in class 9H have for lunch.

a How many students get their lunch from the snack bar? _____

b How many more students have lunch in the canteen than bring a packed lunch? _____

c How many students are there in class 9H?

_____

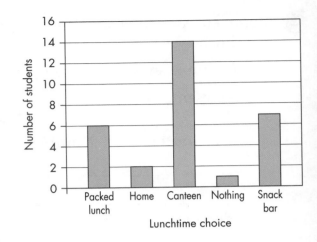

2 Catherine has collected some data about eye colour. Her results are shown in this pie chart. Ten of the people she asked have grey eyes.

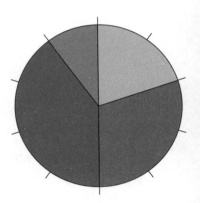

a Which is the most common eye colour? _____

b How many people have green eyes? _____

c How many people have blue eyes? _____

d How many people did she ask altogether? _____

3 The table shows the details of five package holidays.

	Type of accommodation	Number of nights	Price per person	Flight from
Tenerife	Hotel	7	£280	Gatwick
Majorca	Apartment	14	£506	Manchester
Lanzarote	Apartment	7	£385	Gatwick
Algarve	Villa	7	£549	Manchester
Orlando	Hotel	10	£629	Manchester

a How much does it cost per person for the holiday in Lanzarote? £_____

b For how many nights is the holiday in Orlando? _____

c Does the Tenerife holiday fly from Manchester? _____

d Which two resorts are offering holidays in apartments?

_____ and _____

e Which is the most expensive holiday? _____

Exercise 6A   Imperial and metric measures

This exercise will give you practice in

- converting common imperial measures into approximate metric measures

1 Each picture shows an imperial measure. Circle the metric amount which is approximately the same as the imperial amount.

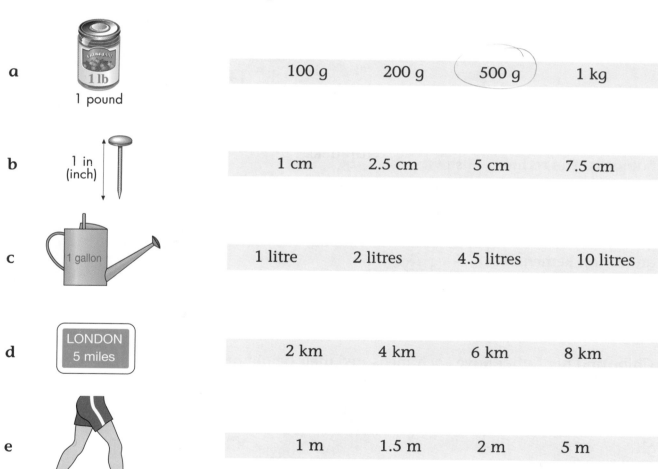

a 1 pound

100 g   200 g   (500 g)   1 kg

b 1 in (inch)

1 cm   2.5 cm   5 cm   7.5 cm

c 1 gallon

1 litre   2 litres   4.5 litres   10 litres

d LONDON 5 miles

2 km   4 km   6 km   8 km

e 1 yard

1 m   1.5 m   2 m   5 m

2 Complete the table to show the conversions between miles and kilometres.

About how many kilometres is 12.5 miles?

_____ km

miles	km
5	8
10	
15	
20	
50	
100	

3 Complete the table to show the conversions between pints and litres.

About how many litres is 35 pints?

_____ litres

pints	litres
1.75	1
3.5	
	3
	4
	5
17.5	

4 Here is a recipe for flapjacks. The recipe gives the amounts of ingredients in ounces (oz). Rewrite the recipe giving the amounts in grams (g). Remember that 1 oz is about 30 grams.

Flapjacks	
butter	4 oz
sugar	2 oz
oats	5 oz
flour	1 oz
syrup	2 tablespoons

Flapjacks	
butter	_____ g
sugar	_____ g
oats	_____ g
flour	_____ g
syrup	2 tablespoons

5 Chloe and her father have each measured their height and weight in imperial units. Convert each measure into metric units. Use a calculator.

Height

65 in ≈ _____ cm = _____ m

Weight

130 lb ≈ _____ g = _____ kg

Height

71 in ≈ _____ cm = _____ m

Weight

165 lb ≈ _____ g = _____ kg

Exercise 6B Area of rectangles and compound shapes

This exercise will give you practice in

- working out the area of a rectangle using the formula
  area of rectangle = length × width or $A = l \times w$
- working out the area of compound shapes made up of rectangles

1 Work out the area of each rectangle using the formula $A = l \times w$.

a
7 cm
3 cm

$A =$ _____

$A =$ _____ cm^2

b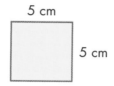
5 cm
5 cm

$A =$ _____

$A =$ _____ cm^2

c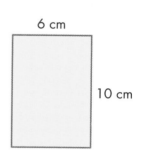
6 cm
10 cm

$A =$ _____

$A =$ _____ cm^2

d
8 cm
4 cm

$A =$ _____

$A =$ _____ cm^2

e
3 cm
11 cm

$A =$ _____

$A =$ _____ cm^2

f
10 cm
3.5 cm

$A =$ _____

$A =$ _____ cm^2

2 Complete the table using the formula $A = l \times w$. Give the correct units for each area.

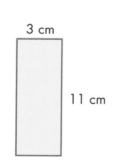

l	w	A
7 cm	11 cm	
4 m	15 m	
10 cm	25 cm	
13 km	4 km	
12 cm	32 cm	

3 Divide each of the following shapes into rectangles. Work out the area of each rectangle then find the total area of the shape. The first one has been started for you.

a

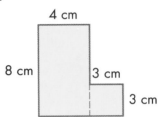

b

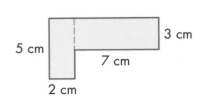

c

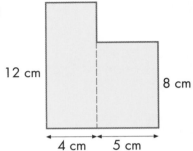

$A =$ __8 × 4__ + __3 × 3__

$A =$ _____ + _____

$A =$ _____ cm^2

$A =$ _____ + _____

$A =$ _____ + _____

$A =$ _____ cm^2

$A =$ _____ + _____

$A =$ _____ + _____

$A =$ _____ cm^2

d

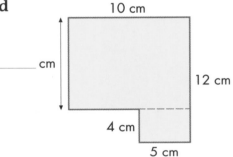

e

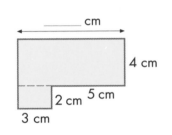

f

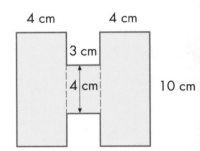

$A =$ _____ + _____

$A =$ _____ + _____

$A =$ _____ cm^2

$A =$ _____ + _____

$A =$ _____ + _____

$A =$ _____ cm^2

$A =$ _____ + _____ + _____

$A =$ _____ + _____ + _____

$A =$ _____ cm^2

4 Find the unknown length or width for each rectangle.

a

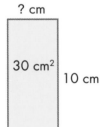

b

c

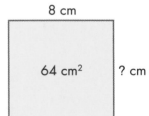

d

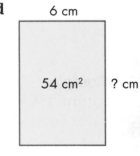

_____ cm

_____ cm

_____ cm

_____ cm

Exercise 6C   Area of triangles

This exercise will give you practice in

- working out the area of a triangle using various methods, including the formula:

    area of triangle = $\frac{1}{2}$ of base × height or $A = \frac{1}{2} \times b \times h$

1 Work out the area of each triangle by counting squares. Each square represents 1 square centimetre.

a
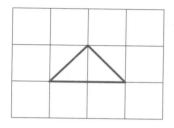

b
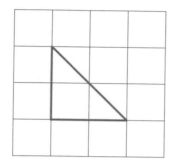

c
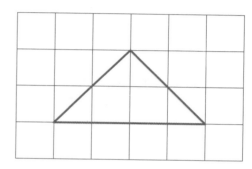

Area _____ cm^2 Area _____ cm^2 Area _____ cm^2

d
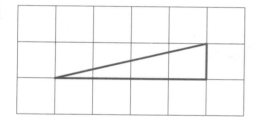

e
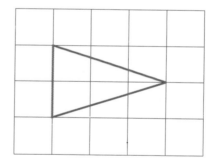

Area _____ cm^2 Area _____ cm^2

2 Work out the area of each triangle by first finding the area of the rectangle that encloses it. Each square represents 1 square centimetre.

a
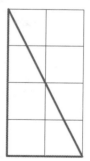

b
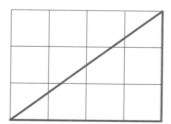

Area of rectangle = _____ cm^2 Area of rectangle = _____ cm^2

Area of triangle = _____ cm^2 Area of triangle = _____ cm^2

c
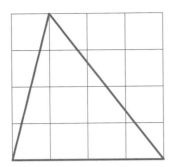

d
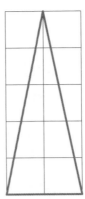

Area of rectangle = _____ cm^2

Area of triangle = _____ cm^2

Area of rectangle = _____ cm^2

Area of triangle = _____ cm^2

3 Use the formula to work out the area of each right-angled triangle.

a
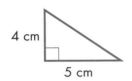

_____

_____

b
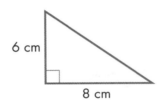

_____

_____

c
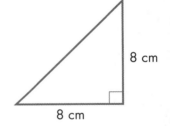

_____

_____

d
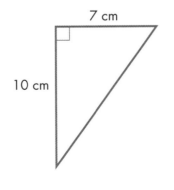

_____

_____

e
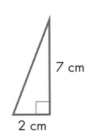

_____

_____

f
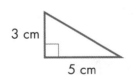

_____

_____

4 Use the formula to work out the area of each triangle.

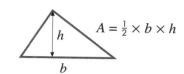

$A = \frac{1}{2} \times b \times h$

a

3 cm
4 cm

_____
_____

b

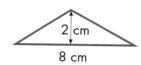

2 cm
8 cm

_____
_____

c

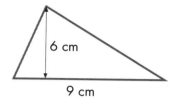

6 cm
9 cm

_____
_____

d

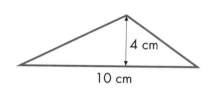

4 cm
10 cm

_____
_____

e

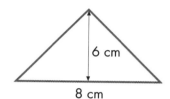

6 cm
8 cm

_____
_____

f

10 cm
3 cm

_____
_____

Exercise 6D Area of parallelograms

This exercise will give you practice in

- working out the area of a parallelogram by making it into a rectangle
- working out the area of a parallelogram using the formula
  area of parallelogram = base × height or $A = b \times h$

1 Work out the area of each of these parallelograms.

a

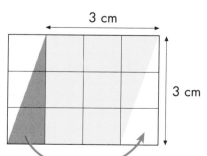

3 cm

3 cm

Area = _____ cm × _____ cm

= _____ cm²

b

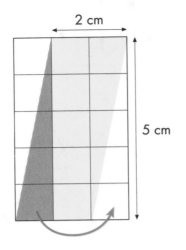

Area = _____ cm × _____ cm

= _____ cm²

c

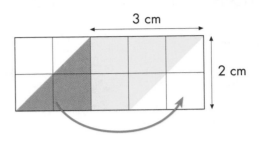

Area = _____ cm × _____ cm

= _____ cm²

2 Use the formula $A = b \times h$ to work out the area of each parallelogram.

a

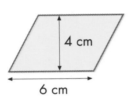

4 cm

6 cm

$A =$ _____ × _____

= _____ cm²

b

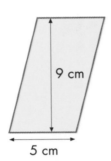

9 cm

5 cm

$A =$ _____ × _____

= _____ cm²

c

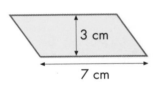

3 cm

7 cm

$A =$ _____ × _____

= _____ cm²

d

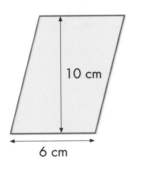

10 cm

6 cm

$A =$ _____

= _____ cm²

e

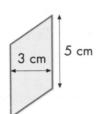

3 cm

5 cm

$A =$ _____

= _____ cm²

f

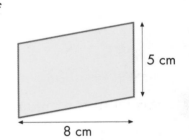

5 cm

8 cm

$A =$ _____

= _____ cm²

3 On squared paper draw **three** different parallelograms which have an area of 6 cm².

Exercise 7A   Powers of 10

This exercise will give you practice in
- reading and writing numbers as powers of 10

1 Complete each of these statements.

a $10^0 = 1$ b $10^1 = 10$

c $10^2 = 10 \times 10 =$ _____

d $10^3 = 10 \times 10 \times 10 =$ _____

e $10^4 =$ _____ $=$ _____

f $10^5 =$ _____ $=$ _____

g $10^6 =$ _____ $=$ _____

2 Draw lines to match the corresponding values below.

one 10^6

one thousand 10^1

ten thousand 10^3

one hundred thousand 10^5

one hundred 10^2

ten 10^4

one million 10^0

3 Work out each of these multiplications.

a $3 \times 10^2 = 3 \times 100 =$ _____

b $7 \times 10^4 = 7 \times 10\,000 =$ _____

c $4 \times 10^3 = 4 \times$ _____ $=$ _____

d $2 \times 10^5 = 2 \times$ _____ $=$ _____

e $8 \times 10^3 =$ _____ $=$ _____

f $9 \times 10^6 =$ _____ $=$ _____

4 Write each of your answers to Question **3** in words.

a _____   b _____

c _____   d _____

e _____   f _____

5 Work out each of these multiplications.

a $3.4 \times 10^3 = 3.4 \times 1000 = $ _____

b $1.7 \times 10^2 = 1.7 \times 100 = $ _____

c $8.8 \times 10^4 = 8.8 \times $ _____ $ = $ _____

d $2.3 \times 10^6 = 2.3 \times $ _____ $ = $ _____

e $3.7 \times 10^2 = $ _____ $ = $ _____

f $2.9 \times 10^1 = $ _____ $ = $ _____

Exercise 7B Column addition of whole numbers and decimals

This exercise will give you practice in
- adding whole numbers and decimal numbers

1 Work out the answer to each addition.

a $357 + 89$ b $797 + 278$ c $889 + 398$

d $1567 + 367$ e $46 + 78 + 125$ f $67 + 675 + 185$

Work out the answer to each addition.

a   3.46 + 5.52

b   4.58 + 8.79

c   12.65 + 11.37

d   4 + 0.7 + 1.6

e   3.6 + 1.45 + 5

f   7.7 + 19 + 6.87

27	9
8	13

4.7	15.4
3.8	9.9

3.24	9.27
1.76	4.32

Choose one number from each of the three boxes and add the three numbers together.
Repeat this as many times as you can, choosing three different numbers each time.

Exercise 7C Column subtraction of whole numbers and decimals

This exercise will give you practice in

- subtracting whole numbers and decimal numbers

 1 Work out the answer to each subtraction.

a 457 – 234

b 567 – 129

c 560 – 276

d 872 – 595

e 1867 – 868

f 2567 – 1459

 2 Work out the answer to each subtraction.

a 28.9 – 14.7

b 32.3 – 16.9

c 5.68 – 3.79

d 23.56 – 18.57

e 43.86 – 22.3

f 98.9 – 45.73

g 195.5 – 78.56

h 47 – 27.45

i 123.9 – 78.69

Exercise 7D   Column multiplication of whole numbers and decimals

This exercise will give you practice in
- multiplying whole numbers and decimal numbers

1 Work out the answer to each of these multiplication calculations.

a 35×7

b 428×8

c 768×4

d 4364×6

e 73.8×4

f 3.93×5

g 23.51×9

h 4.087×6

2 Work out the answer to each multiplication.

a 57×4

b 69×9

c 237×6

d 8×256

e 1984×5

f 6.8×7

g 45.98×3

h 8×459.7

i 32.08×9

3 Use the digits 4, 7, 8 and 9 to make up four multiplication questions. Use each digit once only in each calculation. Work out your answer.

a □□□
    × □
    ____
    □□□□

b □.□□
    × □
    ____
    □□□

c □.□□
    × □
    ____
    □□□

d □□.□
    × □
    ____
    □□□□

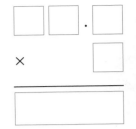

Exercise 7E   Column division of whole numbers and decimals

This exercise will give you practice in

o dividing whole numbers and decimal numbers

1 Work out the answer to each division calculation. Use a separate sheet of paper if you need more spaces.

a 4⟌5 6

b 5⟌7 5

c 6⟌8 4

d 7⟌9 1

e 4⟌1 0 8

f 6⟌1 9 2

2 Work out the answer to each division.

a $207 \div 9$

b $342 \div 6$

c $826 \div 7$

3 Work out each division. Each answer has a remainder. Use a separate sheet of paper if you need more space.

a 6⟌8 0

b 4⟌8 7

c 5⟌1 0 8

d 7⟌9 4

e 8⟌1 2 6

f 7⟌2 3 4

4 Work out each division. Each answer has a remainder.

    a $121 \div 9$ **b** $307 \div 4$ **c** $461 \div 8$

 5 Work out the answer to each division calculation. Use a separate sheet of paper if you need more space.

    a $5\overline{)6.5}$ **b** $6\overline{)8.4}$ **c** $7\overline{)9.1}$

    d $6\overline{)13.8}$ **e** $8\overline{)42.4}$ **f** $4\overline{)2.36}$

    g $6\overline{)0.72}$ **h** $4\overline{)3.08}$ **i** $9\overline{)0.909}$

Exercise 7F   Real-life problems

This exercise will give you practice in

- solving problems using addition, subtraction, multiplication and division of whole and decimal numbers

For each question show your working. Set out your calculations.

 1   What is the difference between 746 and 389?

 2   What is the sum of 139 and 276?

 3   There are 365 days in a year. How many days are there in 4 years?

4 Eggs are packed in boxes of six. How many boxes are needed to pack 318 eggs?

5 Joe completes nine laps of the running track. One lap measures 375 metres. How far did Joe run altogether?

6 Mia has a bag of flour containing 1.4 kg. She uses 0.56 kg to make some bread. How much flour is left?

7 Amy and Kylie have gone out for lunch.

a Amy has a pizza and salad. How much does she pay altogether?

MENU

Curry	£1.85
Lasagne	£3.20
Pizza	£2.79
Salad	£1.27
Apple pie	£1.95
Fudge cake	£2.09

b Kylie has lasagne followed by fudge cake. How much does she pay for both?

c How much more expensive was Kylie's meal than Amy's?

Exercise 8A   Divisibility and multiples

This exercise will give you practice in
- finding and recognising multiples of whole numbers

1 Write down the first **five** multiples of these numbers.

    a 3 _____   **b** 5 _____

    c 6 _____   **d** 8 _____

    e 13 _____   **f** 20 _____

    g 35 _____   **h** 51 _____

2 Write the next **two** multiples of 4 after 52.   _____ , _____

3 Write the next **two** multiples of 12 after 48.   _____ , _____

4 Circle the number which is **not** a multiple of 4.

    8   14   20   32   44

5 Circle the number which is **not** a multiple of 6.

    12   22   24   42   54

6 Shade the squares containing numbers that are multiples of 9.
Which letter have you shaded? _____

22	63	108	9
17	72	23	80
3	45	81	43
44	18	40	61
7	99	20	14

7 In the list of numbers below cross out any multiples of 5 and any multiples of 7.

5   14   30   33   42   45   49   75   80   84

Which number is left? _____   Which number is this a multiple of? _____

Exercise 8B   Factors of numbers

This exercise will give you practice in
- finding and recognising factors of whole numbers

1 Write each number as different pairs of factors.

a

b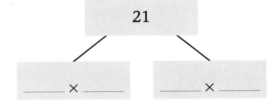

c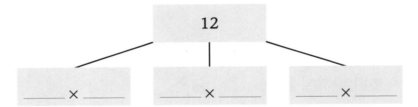

d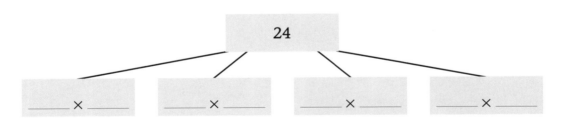

2 Write down all of the factors of each number.

a   20 _____   b   30 _____

c   36 _____

3 Circle the number which is **not** a factor of 10.

1   2   5   10   20

4 Circle the number which is **not** a factor of 12.

1   3   6   8   12

5 Shade the factors of 24.

Shade the factors of 50.

Shade the factors of 14.

What letter do the unshaded squares make? _____

1	9	20	48	3
7	37	4	14	6
50	60	51	11	5
2	12	10	13	25
8	15	21	17	24

6 In the list of numbers below cross out any factors of 10, 22 and 30.

1   2   3   4   5   6   9   10   11   14   15   22   27   30

Which numbers are left? _____

Exercise 8C   Highest common factors and lowest common multiples

This exercise will give you practice in

- finding common factors, including the highest common factor of two numbers
- finding common multiples, including the lowest common multiple of two numbers

1 List all of the factors of 8.   _____

List all of the factors of 10.   _____

Circle the factors which appear in both lists and complete these sentences.

The common factors of 8 and 10 are _____ and _____.

The highest common factor of 8 and 10 is _____.

2 List all of the factors of 12. _____

List all of the factors of 20. _____

Circle the factors which appear in both lists and complete these sentences.

The common factors of 12 and 20 are _____, _____ and _____.

The highest common factor of 12 and 20 is _____.

3 Circle the numbers which are multiples of 4 in red. Circle the numbers which are multiples of 3 in blue.

6   15   12   30   24   27   8

Which two numbers are multiples of both 3 and 4? _____ and _____.

4 Circle the numbers which are multiples of 5 in red. Circle the numbers which are multiples of 2 in blue.

10   15   45   38   16   25   30

Which two numbers are multiples of both 2 and 5? _____ and _____.

5 List the first six multiples of 2. _____

List the first six multiples of 3. _____

Circle the multiples which appear in both lists. Complete these sentences.

Some common multiples of 2 and 3 are _____.

The lowest common multiple of 2 and 3 is _____.

6 List the first 10 multiples of 4. _____

List the first 10 multiples of 5. _____

Circle the multiples which appear in both lists. Complete these sentences.

Some common multiples of 4 and 5 are _____.

The lowest common multiple of 4 and 5 is _____.

Exercise 8D   Prime numbers

This exercise will give you practice in

● recognising prime numbers

1 Shade in 1.

Shade all of the multiples of 2 except 2.

Shade all of the multiples of 3 except 3.

Shade all of the multiples of 5 except 5.

Shade all of the multiples of 7 except 7.

All of the unshaded numbers are **prime numbers**.

1	2	3	4	5	6	7	8	9	10
11	12	13	14	15	16	17	18	19	20
21	22	23	24	25	26	27	28	29	30
31	32	33	34	35	36	37	38	39	40
41	42	43	44	45	46	47	48	49	50
51	52	53	54	55	56	57	58	59	60
61	62	63	64	65	66	67	68	69	70
71	72	73	74	75	76	77	78	79	80
81	82	83	84	85	86	87	88	89	90
91	92	93	94	95	96	97	98	99	100

2 Complete these sentences.

The only even prime number is _____. All of the other prime numbers are _____.

Prime numbers have only two _____, 1 and the number itself.

3 Circle the numbers which are **not** prime.

2   4   5   8   9   11   13   16   17

4 Put these numbers into the Venn diagram.

2   7   17   23   25   27   31   33   40

prime   greater than 20

5 Write each of these non-prime numbers as a product of two or three prime numbers.

a $4 = $ _____ × _____ **b** $6 = $ _____ × _____ **c** $9 = $ _____ × _____

d $10 = $ _____ × _____ **e** $14 = $ _____ × _____ **f** $15 = $ _____ × _____

g $8 = $ _____ × _____ × _____ **h** $12 = $ _____ × _____ × _____

i $18 = $ _____ × _____ × _____ **j** $20 = $ _____ × _____ × _____

Exercise 8E Square numbers

This exercise will give you practice in

- recognising and finding square numbers

1 Complete each of the following.

$1^2 = 1 \times 1 = 1$ $2^2 = 2 \times 2 = $ _____

$3^2 = $ _____ × _____ = _____ $4^2 = $ _____ = _____

$5^2 = $ _____ = _____ $6^2 = $ _____ = _____

$7^2 = $ _____ = _____ $8^2 = $ _____ = _____

$9^2 = $ _____ = _____ $10^2 = $ _____ = _____

$11^2 = $ _____ = _____ $12^2 = $ _____ = _____

2 Complete these sentences.

a The sixth square number is _____. **b** The _____ square number is 121.

c The ninth square number is _____.

3 Colour **yellow** the squares which contain **even** square numbers.
Colour **red** the squares which contain **odd** square numbers.
Colour **green** the squares which do not contain square numbers.
You should have made a symmetrical pattern.

1	7	20	14	56
130	81	100	3	80
79	4	9	36	90
44	18	64	49	32
101	73	61	48	25

4 Circle the numbers which are **not** squares.

a 16 25 (38) 49 64 **b** 64 81 (99) 121 144

Exercise 8F   Square roots

This exercise will give you practice in

- recognising and finding square roots of numbers

1 Complete each of the following.

The square of 1 is 1 × 1 = 1.   The square root of 1 is 1.

The square of 2 is 2 × 2 = 4.   The square root of 4 is 2.

The square of 3 is __3__ × __3__ = __9__.   The square root of __9__ is 3.

The square of 4 is __4__ × __4__ = __16__.   The square root of __16__ is 4.

The square of 5 is __5__ × __5__ = __25__.   The square root of __25__ is __5__.

The square of 6 is __6__ × __6__ = __36__.   The square root of __81__ is __9__.

The square of 7 is __7__ × __7__ = __49__.   The square root of __100__ is __10__.

The square of 8 is __8__ × __8__ = __64__.   The square root of __121__ is __11__.

The square of 9 is __9__ × __9__ = __81__.   The square root of __144__ is __12__.

The square of 10 is __10__ × __10__ = __100__.   The square root of __49__ is __7__.

The square of 11 is __11__ × __11__ = __121__.   The square root of __64__ is __8__.

The square of 12 is __12__ × __12__ = __144__.   The square root of __36__ is __6__.

2 Write down the square roots of each of the following.

a $\sqrt{36}$ = __6__   **b** $\sqrt{25}$ = __5__   **c** $\sqrt{100}$ = __10__

d $\sqrt{81}$ = __9__   **e** $\sqrt{1}$ = __1__   **f** $\sqrt{64}$ = __8__

g $\sqrt{9}$ = __3__   **h** $\sqrt{4}$ = __2__   **i** $\sqrt{49}$ = __7__

j $\sqrt{16}$ = __4__   **k** $\sqrt{121}$ = __11__   **l** $\sqrt{144}$ = __12__

3 Find each of the following square roots.

a $\sqrt{3136}$ = _____   **b** $\sqrt{1764}$ = _____   **c** $\sqrt{784}$ = _____

d $\sqrt{841}$ = _____   **e** $\sqrt{1936}$ = _____   **f** $\sqrt{1089}$ = _____

Exercise 8G   Cube numbers

This exercise will give you practice in
- recognising and finding cube numbers

1 Complete each of the following.

$1^3 = 1 \times 1 \times 1 = 1$

$2^3 \; = 2 \times 2 \times 2 =$ _____

$3^3 \; =$ _____ $\times$ _____ $\times$ _____ $=$ _____

$4^3 \; =$ _____ $=$ _____

$5^3 \; =$ _____ $=$ _____

$6^3 \; =$ _____ $=$ _____

$7^3 \; =$ _____ $=$ _____

$8^3 \; =$ _____ $=$ _____

$9^3 \; =$ _____ $=$ _____

$10^3 =$ _____ $=$ _____

2 Write down the answers for each of the following.

a $7^3 =$ _____   **b** $2^3 =$ _____   **c** $4^3 =$ _____

d $5^3 =$ _____   **e** $10^3 =$ _____   **f** $9^3 =$ _____

g $1^3 =$ _____   **h** $6^3 =$ _____   **i** $3^3 =$ _____

3 Complete these sentences.

a _____ is the fifth cube number.   **b** The eighth cube number is _____.

c 64 is the _____ cube number.   **d** The next cube number after 729 is _____.

4 Circle the number which is **not** a cube number.

8   64   100   216   512   729

5 Work out each of the following cube numbers.

a $11^3 =$ _____   **b** $12^3 =$ _____   **c** $14^3 =$ _____

d $18^3 =$ _____   **e** $20^3 =$ _____   **f** $25^3 =$ _____

g $40^3 =$ _____   **h** $50^3 =$ _____   **i** $100^3 =$ _____

Exercise 8H   Cube roots

This exercise will give you practice in

- recognising and finding cube roots of numbers

1 Complete each of the following.

The cube of 1 is $1 \times 1 \times 1 = 1$.

The cube of 2 is $2 \times 2 \times 2 = 8$.

The cube of 3 is _____ × _____ × _____ = _____.

The cube of 4 is _____ × _____ × _____ = _____.

The cube of 5 is _____ × _____ × _____ = _____.

The cube of 6 is _____ × _____ × _____ = _____.

The cube of 7 is _____ × _____ × _____ = _____.

The cube of 8 is _____ × _____ × _____ = _____.

The cube of 9 is _____ × _____ × _____ = _____.

The cube of 10 is _____ × _____ × _____ = _____.

The cube root of 1 is 1.

The cube root of 8 is 2.

The cube root of _____ is 3.

The cube root of _____ is 4.

The cube root of _____ is _____.

The cube root of _____ is _____.

The cube root of _____ is _____.

The cube root of _____ is _____.

The cube root of _____ is _____.

The cube root of _____ is _____.

2 Work out each of these cube roots.

a $\sqrt[3]{8} =$ _____

b $\sqrt[3]{64} =$ _____

c $\sqrt[3]{1} =$ _____

d $\sqrt[3]{1000} =$ _____

e $\sqrt[3]{125} =$ _____

f $\sqrt[3]{343} =$ _____

g $\sqrt[3]{27} =$ _____

h $\sqrt[3]{512} =$ _____

i $\sqrt[3]{216} =$ _____

j $\sqrt[3]{729} =$ _____

3 Complete these sentences.

a The cube root of 64 is _____.

b The number that must be cubed to give 1000 is _____.

c _____ is the cube root of 343.

d _____ cubed is equal to 512.

4 Work out each of these cube roots.

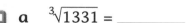

a $\sqrt[3]{1331} =$ _____

b $\sqrt[3]{3375} =$ _____

c $\sqrt[3]{4096} =$ _____

d $\sqrt[3]{1728} =$ _____

e $\sqrt[3]{2197} =$ _____

f $\sqrt[3]{6859} =$ _____

g $\sqrt[3]{8000} =$ _____

h $\sqrt[3]{9261} =$ _____

i $\sqrt[3]{15\,625} =$ _____

Exercise 9A Probability scales

This exercise will give you practice in
- positioning events on a probability scale

1 Draw arrows on the probability scale to indicate the likelihood of each of these events. The first one has been done for you.

Impossible   Very unlikely   Unlikely   Even   Likely   Very likely   Certain

a It will snow in December.

b Someone in your class will arrive late for school today.

c You will live to be 300 years old.

d The next baby born will be a boy.

e The next person to come into the room will be left-handed.

f You will die one day.

g You will catch a cold this year.

2 Work out the probability of each event, giving your answer as a fraction. Draw an arrow to show its position on the probability scale.

0 $\frac{1}{4}$ $\frac{1}{2}$ $\frac{3}{4}$ 1

a Probability of a flipped coin landing on Heads = _____

b Probability of a rolled dice landing on 7 = _____

c Probability of spinning a 3 on this spinner = _____

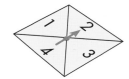

d Probability of a rolled dice landing on a number from 1 to 6 = _____

e Probability of spinning an even number on this spinner = _____

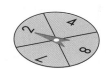

3 Kyle has a bag of coloured counters. Work out the probability of each event, giving your answer as a fraction. Remember that probability fractions are always cancelled down.

a Probability of picking a green counter = _____ = _____

b Probability of picking a red counter = _____

c Probability of picking a yellow counter = _____

d Probability of picking a blue counter = _____

e Probability of picking a red or yellow counter = _____ = _____

Exercise 9B   Calculating probabilities

This exercise will give you practice in

- working out the probability of an event **not** occurring $(1 - p)$ from the probability that the event will occur (p)

1 A bag contains three red counters and four green counters.

The probability of picking a green counter = $\frac{4}{7}$

The probability of picking a red counter = _____

2 A box of plastic shapes contains three triangles and seven stars.

The probability of picking a star = _____

The probability of picking a triangle = _____

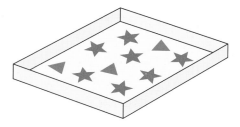

3 This spinner can land on 1 or 2.

The probability of landing on 1 = _____

The probability of landing on 2 = _____

4 A bag contains one yellow, two red and two green counters.

The probability of picking a green counter = _____

The probability of picking a counter that is **not** green = _____

5 This spinner can land on the numbers 1 to 8.

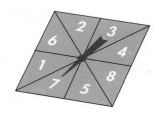

The probability of landing on 7 = _____

The probability of **not** landing on 7 = _____

6 The probability that a flipped coin lands on Heads is $\frac{1}{2}$.

What is the probability that the coin does **not** land on Heads? _____

7 The probability of getting a 3 on a normal dice is $\frac{1}{6}$.

What is the probability that the dice will **not** land on 3? _____

8 The probability of picking a red counter from a bag of coloured counters is $\frac{3}{10}$.

What is the probability of **not** picking a red counter? _____

9 The probability that it will rain tomorrow is $\frac{1}{7}$.

What is the probability that it will **not** rain tomorrow? _____

10 The probability that the local football team will win their next game is $\frac{8}{11}$

What is the probability that the team will **not** win their next game? _____

11 The probability that Kerry will pass her maths exam is $\frac{7}{15}$.

What is the probability that Kerry will **not** pass the exam? _____

12 The probability of winning first prize in a raffle is $\frac{1}{100}$.

What is the probability of **not** winning first prize? _____

Exercise 9C   Experimental probability 1

This exercise will give you practice in

- recognising that repeating an experiment usually gives different outcomes

1 **a**   Put a red counter, a blue counter and a yellow counter in a bag or box. Take a counter out at random (without looking). Record the colour in the tally chart. Put the counter back and repeat this 30 times.

Colour	Tally	Frequency
Red		
Blue		
Yellow		

What is the experimental probability of picking

i   a red counter? _____

ii   a blue counter? _____

iii   a yellow counter? _____

b   Now repeat the experiment and record your results in the tally chart below.

Colour	Tally	Frequency
Red		
Blue		
Yellow		

What is the experimental probability of picking

i   a red counter? _____

ii   a blue counter? _____

iii   a yellow counter? _____

c   Write a comment about your results in parts **a** and **b**.

_____

_____

2 **a** If you flip a coin 20 times how many times would you expect it to land on

    i Heads? _____

    ii Tails? _____

  b **i** Flip a coin 20 times and record your results in the tally chart.

	Tally	Frequency
Heads		
Tails		

    ii Did you get the same number of Heads and Tails as you predicted in part **a**? _____

  c **i** Repeat your experiment and record your results in the tally chart.

	Tally	Frequency
Heads		
Tails		

    ii Did you get the same results for this experiment as you did in part **b**? _____

3 **a** If you roll a dice 60 times how many times would you expect it to land on

    i 1? _____   **ii** 2? _____   **iii** 3? _____

    iv 4? _____   **v** 5? _____   **vi** 6? _____

  b **i** Roll a dice 60 times and record your results in the tally chart.

Number	Tally	Frequency
1		
2		
3		
4		
5		
6		

    ii Did your results match your expectations? _____

c i Repeat your experiment and record your results in the tally chart.

Number	Tally	Frequency
1		
2		
3		
4		
5		
6		

ii Did you get the same results for this experiment as you did for the first one? _____

Exercise 9D   Experimental probability 2

This exercise will give you practice in

- recognising that increasing the number of times an experiment is repeated generally gives more accurate estimates of probability

1 a Drop a drawing pin 10 times. Record your results using the tally chart.

	Tally	Frequency
Point up		
Point down		

Using your results, what is the probability of the pin landing point up?

Give your answer as a fraction. _____

b Repeat your experiment but this time drop the drawing pin 50 times. Record your results using the tally chart.

	Tally	Frequency
Point up		
Point down		

Using your results, what is the probability of the pin landing point up?

Give your answer as a fraction. _____

c You have worked out two values for the probability that a pin lands point up.

Which do you think is more accurate? _____

2 **a** **i** Flip a coin 20 times. Record your results using the tally chart.

	Tally	Frequency
Heads		
Tails		

ii Using your results, what is the probability of the coin landing on Tails? Give your answer as a fraction and as a decimal.

Fraction _____   Decimal _____

b **i** Working in pairs repeat the experiment but this time flip the coin 100 times. Record your results using the tally chart.

	Tally	Frequency
Heads		
Tails		

ii Using your results, what is the probability of the coin landing on Tails? Give your answer as a fraction and as a decimal.

Fraction _____   Decimal _____

c You know that the **theoretical** probability of a coin landing on Tails is $\frac{1}{2}$ or 0.5. Which of your experiments, **a** or **b**, gives the more accurate answer? _____

Exercise 10A Line symmetry and reflection

This exercise will give you practice in

- identifying the line symmetry in 2-D shapes

1 All of these shapes have line symmetry. Draw the lines of symmetry on each shape.

a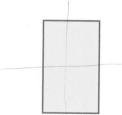

b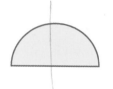

c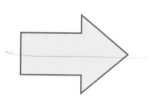

d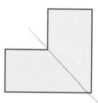

e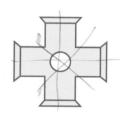

f

g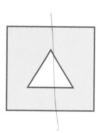

h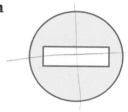

2 Some of these shapes do not have line symmetry. Put a tick inside the shapes that have line symmetry. Put a cross inside those that do not.

a

b

c

d

e

f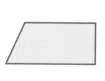

3 Add an extra square to give the shape:

a four lines of symmetry.

b one line of symmetry.

c no lines of symmetry.

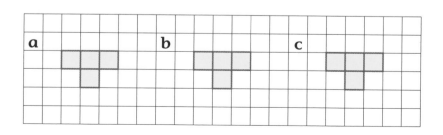

4 **a** Shade in squares to give the shape one line of symmetry.

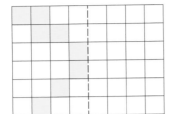

b Shade in squares to give the shape two lines of symmetry.

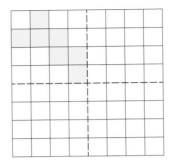

Exercise 10B Rotation symmetry

This exercise will give you practice in

○ identifying the rotation symmetry in 2-D shapes

1 Trace each shape using tracing paper. Rotate the shape about the dot in the centre and work out the order of rotation symmetry.

a

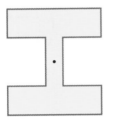

b

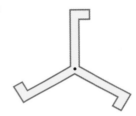

c

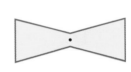

d

e

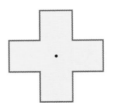

f

2 Some shapes do not have rotation symmetry (order of 1). Put a tick inside the shapes that have rotation symmetry of more than 1 and a cross inside those that do not.

a

b

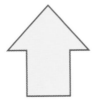

c

d

e f g

3 Write down the order of rotation symmetry of each design.

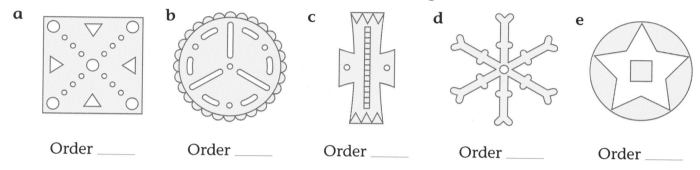

a Order _____ b Order _____ c Order _____ d Order _____ e Order _____

4 Complete these shapes so they have rotation symmetry of the given order.

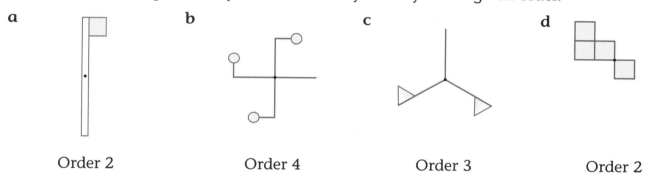

a Order 2 b Order 4 c Order 3 d Order 2

Exercise 10C Scale drawings

This exercise will give you practice in

● working out the dimensions for, and drawing, scale diagrams

1 This is a scale drawing of the shape on the right.

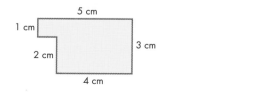

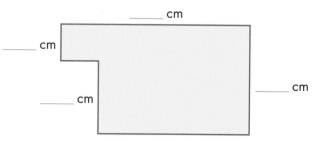

The scale that has been used to draw it is
1 cm to 2 cm.

Complete the lengths of the sides on the actual drawing.

2 A scale drawing of a shape has been made using the scale **1 cm to 3 cm**.
Complete the table below.

Length of line on scale drawing	Actual length of line
2 cm	
5 cm	
10 cm	
7 cm	
	12 cm
	18 cm
	3 cm
	60 cm

3 The shapes below are drawn to scale. For each of the shapes, measure the
sides and draw it to its full size on centimetre-square paper.

a    b    c   d

Scale: 1 cm to 3 cm   Scale: 1 cm to 2 cm   Scale: 1 cm to 3 cm   Scale: 1 cm to 2 cm

Exercise 10D Coordinates in all four quadrants

This exercise will give you practice in

- naming and plotting points in all four quadrants on an *x–y* grid

1 Match these coordinates to the points marked on the grid with letters.

a   (–4, –2) _____   b   (2, 2) _____   c   (–2, –4) _____

d   (3, –2) _____   e   (4, 0) _____   f   (–2, 4) _____

g   (0, –3) _____   h   (3, 5) _____   i   (2, –5) _____

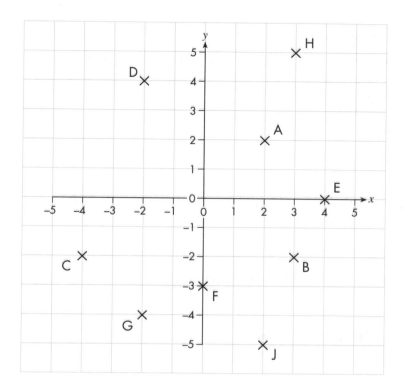

2 Plot the following points on the grid. Join the points with a ruler as you plot them.

(2, 4)   (4, 2)   (4, −1)   (2, −3)   (−1, −3)   (−3, −1)   (−3, 2)   (−1, 4)   (2, 4)

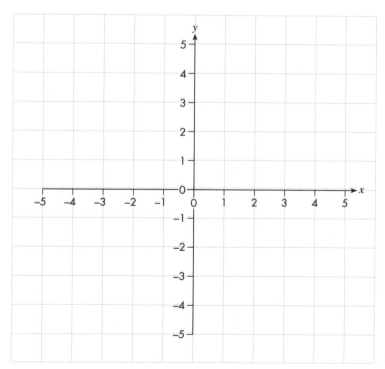

Name the shape you have drawn. _____

3 Each set of coordinates below gives three of the four corners of a rectangle.

On squared paper, draw a coordinate grid for each set (from –6 to +6 on both axes), plot the points and join them with a ruler. Complete the rectangle and write down the coordinates of the fourth corner below.

a   (–3, 3) (5, 3) (5, –2) _____

b   (–2, 2) (1, 5) (3, 3) _____

4 Draw a coordinate grid from –6 to +6 on both axes and plot each set of points, joining them to form a straight line.

a   (4, 4) (2, 2) (0, 0) (–3, –3) (–5, –5)

What do you notice about the coordinates?

_____

b   (–3, –6) (–1, –2) (1, 2) (2, 4) (3, 6)

What do you notice about the coordinates?

_____

Exercise 11A   BODMAS

This exercise will give you practice in

 o using BODMAS (Brackets, pOwers, Division and Multiplication, Addition and Subtraction) rules in calculations

1 Complete each of these calculations.

 a $6 + 3 \times 4 =$ ___9___ + _____ = _____

 b $44 + 20 \div 5 =$ _____ + _____ = _____

 c $6^2 - 4 \times 6 =$ _____ − _____ = _____

 d $50 - 7 \times 5 =$ _____ − _____ = _____

 e $15 - 32 \div 4 =$ _____ = _____

 f $18 - 3^2 =$ _____ = _____

2 Complete each of these calculations.

 a $3 \times 5 + 2 \times 6 =$ _____ + _____ = _____

 b $5^2 - 7 \times 3 =$ _____ − _____ = _____

 c $8 \times 4 - 16 \div 4 =$ _____ − _____ = _____

 d $30 \div 6 + 4 \times 2 =$ _____ = _____

 e $49 \div 7 + 4^2 =$ _____ = _____

 f $3 \times 9 - 3^2 =$ _____ = _____

3 Complete each of these calculations. Remember – brackets first!

 a $21 \div (5 + 2) =$ _____ ÷ _____ = _____

 b $3 \times (9 - 3) =$ _____ × _____ = _____

 c $(8 - 5) \times (6 + 2) =$ _____ × _____ = _____

 d $5^2 \times (2 + 4) =$ _____ = _____

 e $30 \div (6 - 3) =$ _____ = _____

 f $(29 - 19) \times 4^2 =$ _____ = _____

4 Complete each of these calculations.

a $7 + 3 \times 5 + 2^2 = $ _____ + _____ + _____ = _____

b $6 \times 3 - 8 + 4 \div 2 = $ _____ − _____ + _____ = _____

c $(7 - 3) \times 4 + 3 = $ _____ × _____ + _____ = _____ + _____ = _____

d $19 + (10 - 3) \times 5 = $ _____ + _____ × _____ = _____ + _____ = _____

Exercise 11B　Expanding brackets

> **This exercise will give you practice in**
> ○ using brackets in calculations and in algebra

1 Expand each of the following brackets as shown.

a $3(2 + 4) = 3 \times 2 + 3 \times 4 = $ _____ + _____ = _____

b $5(3 + 5) = 5 \times 3 + 5 \times 5 = $ _____ + _____ = _____

c $4(7 - 5) = 4 \times 7 - 4 \times 5 = $ _____ − _____ = _____

d $5(6 - 5) = 5 \times 6 - 5 \times 5 = $ _____ − _____ = _____

e $4(3 + 6) = $ _____ × _____ + _____ × _____ = _____ + _____ = _____

f $5(4 - 2) = $ _____ × _____ − _____ × _____ = _____ − _____ = _____

g $3(2 + 7) = $ _____ × _____ + _____ × _____ = _____ + _____ = _____

h $4(6 - 2) = $ _____ × _____ − _____ × _____ = _____ − _____ = _____

2 Simplify each of the following.

a $5 \times a = $ _____　　**b** $7 \times b = $ _____　　**c** $9 \times c = $ _____

d $4 \times m = $ _____　　**e** $2 \times n = $ _____　　**f** $8 \times j = $ _____

3 Expand each of the following brackets as shown.

a $4(a + 5) = 4 \times a + 4 \times 5 = $ 4a+20 + 20a + 20　　5(4a +4)

b $3(b + 2) = 3 \times b + 3 \times 2 = $ _____ + _____

c $2(c - 3) = 2 \times c - 2 \times 3 = $ _____ − _____

d $3(d + 4) = $ _____ + _____ = _____ + _____

e $5(e + 6) = $ _____ + _____ = _____ + _____

f $3(f - 7) = $ _____ − _____ = _____ − _____

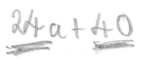

24a + 40

Exercise 11C Solving equations

This exercise will give you practice in

- solving more complex linear equations

1 Fill in the spaces to solve each of the following equations.

a $2x + 3 = 7$

Subtract _____ from both sides

$2x + 3$ _____ $= 7$ _____

$2x =$ _____

Divide both sides by _____

$2x \div$ _____ $=$ _____ $\div$ _____

$x =$ _____

b $3x + 4 = 16$

Subtract _____ from both sides

$3x + 4$ _____ $= 16$ _____

$3x =$ _____

Divide both sides by _____

$3x \div$ _____ $=$ _____ $\div$ _____

$x =$ _____

c $4x + 1 = 9$

Subtract _____ from both sides

$4x + 1$ _____ $= 9$ _____

$4x =$ _____

Divide both sides by _____

$4x \div$ _____ $=$ _____ $\div$ _____

$x =$ _____

d $2x - 3 = 9$

Add _____ to both sides

$2x - 3$ _____ $= 9$ _____

$2x =$ _____

Divide both sides by _____

$2x \div$ _____ $=$ _____ $\div$ _____

$x =$ _____

e $3x - 5 = 13$

Add _____ to both sides

$3x - 5$ _____ $= 13$ _____

$3x =$ _____

Divide both sides by _____

$3x \div$ _____ $=$ _____ $\div$ _____

$x =$ _____

f $4x - 7 = 9$

Add _____ to both sides

$4x - 7$ _____ $= 9$ _____

$4x =$ _____

Divide both sides by _____

$4x \div$ _____ $=$ _____ $\div$ _____

$x =$ _____

2 Solve each of the following equations.

a $2x + 3 = 11$

_____ both sides

_____ = _____

_____ = _____

Divide both sides by _____

$x =$ _____

$x =$ _____

b $3x + 5 = 11$

_____ both sides

_____ = _____

_____ = _____

Divide both sides by _____

$x =$ _____

$x =$ _____

c $5x - 2 = 13$

_____ both sides

_____ = _____

_____ = _____

Divide both sides by _____

$x =$ _____

$x =$ _____

d $6x - 1 = 11$

_____ both sides

_____ = _____

_____ = _____

Divide both sides by _____

$x =$ _____

$x =$ _____

Exercise 11D Real-life graphs

This exercise will give you practice in

○ interpreting real-life graphs

1 This graph is used by a taxi driver to work out the cost of the fare for a journey, depending on how many miles are travelled.

Use the graph to work out:

a the cost of a 3 mile journey. _____

b the cost of a 7 mile journey. _____

c how far you could travel for £6.

_____

d how far you could travel for £12.

_____

e how far you could travel for £11.

_____

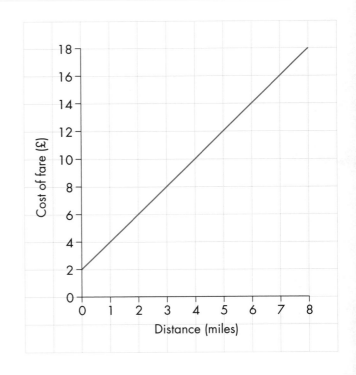

2 The graph on the right shows the distance travelled by Adam on his bike one morning.

Use the graph to answer each of the following.

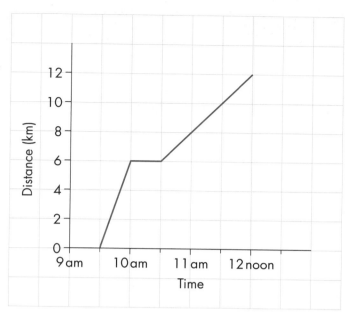

a At what time did Adam set off on

his journey? _____

b How far had Adam travelled

by 10:00 am? _____ km

c Adam had a rest during the journey.

When did he take a rest? _____

d At what time did he complete his

journey? _____

e What is the total distance that Adam

travelled? _____ km

3 The graph shows the maximum temperature for the first 14 days in February.

Use the graph to answer these questions.

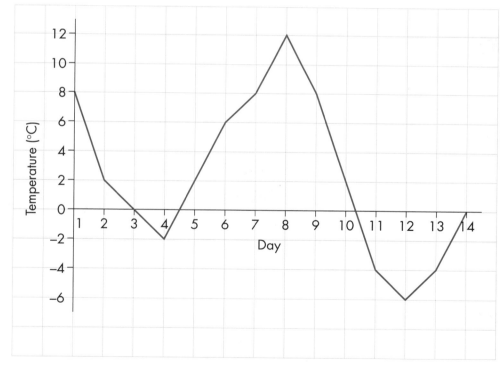

a What was the temperature on 3rd February?

_____ °C

b What was the temperature on 7th February?

_____ °C

c What was the temperature on 10th February?

_____ °C

d What was the temperature on 13th February? _____ °C

e What was the lowest temperature over the 14 days? _____ °C

f What was the highest temperature over the 14 days? _____ °C

g On which days was the maximum temperature –4°C? _____ and _____ February.

Exercise 12A Revision of Number 1

This exercise will help you to revise
- ordering and rounding numbers
- working with decimals, fractions, percentages, ratios and proportions

1 Round each of these numbers to one decimal place.

a   4.75 _____

b   19.08 _____

c   0.42 _____

2 There are 1274 students in Ravi's school. To the nearest hundred, how many students are there in the school? _____

3 Put these decimal numbers in order of size, starting with the smallest.

4.3   4.03   5.4   4.5   0.45   _____

4 Here are the prices of the CD 'Chart Hits 3' in five different stores.

Hitz £13.75	CD World £13.59	Musik £13.97	Sounds £13.95	ABC Disks £13.79

a   In which store is the CD most expensive? _____

b   In which store is the CD on sale at the cheapest price? _____

5 Write the part of the shape that is shaded as a fraction and as a decimal.

a   fraction _____

decimal _____

b   fraction _____

decimal _____

6 Circle the fractions that are equivalent to 0.5.

$\frac{1}{2}$ $\frac{5}{100}$ $\frac{50}{100}$ $\frac{1}{5}$ $\frac{5}{10}$ $\frac{5}{15}$

7 Calculate each of the following, giving your answers as fractions.

    a $\frac{7}{10} - \frac{3}{10} =$ _____   **b** $\frac{2}{3} - \frac{1}{5} =$ _____

8   **a**   Find $\frac{1}{5}$ of 30. _____

    b   There are 30 students in Paul's class. $\frac{3}{5}$ of them are boys.

         Use your answer to part **a** to help you work out how many boys are in Paul's class.

_____

9 Work out each of the following.

    a $\frac{1}{8} \times 56$ _____   **b** $24 \times \frac{2}{3}$ _____   **c** $7 \div \frac{1}{5}$ _____

10   **a**   What is 1% of £800? _____

    b   Use your answer to part **a** to find:

        i   3% of £800. _____   **ii**   13% of £800. _____

11 Use a calculator to find 23% of 124. _____

12 Simplify these ratios, giving your answers in their simplest terms.

    a   2 : 8   **b**   15 : 10   **c**   3 : 18   **d**   16 : 4

    _____   _____   _____   _____

13 Bethany is mixing yellow and red paint to make orange paint. She mixes two tins of yellow paint for every one tin of red paint.

    a   How many tins of yellow paint would she need to mix with four tins of red? _____

    b   How many tins of red paint would she need to mix with six tins of yellow? _____

    c   Bethany uses 15 tins of paint altogether. How many tins of each colour does she use?

         _____ tins of yellow   _____ tins of red

Exercise 12B   Revision of Number 2

This exercise will help you to revise

- using the four rules of number for calculations and to solve problems

1 Work out the answers to each of these. Make jottings on rough paper if you need to.

a 19 + 29 = _____

b 43 + 47 = _____

c 139 + 42 = _____

d 38 – 17 = _____

e 75 – 26 = _____

f 200 – 138 = _____

g 8 × 7 = _____

h 20 × 6 = _____

i 3 × 15 = _____

2 Find two different pairs of numbers to make this statement true.

$\boxed{} \times \boxed{} = 54$ 　　　　　$\boxed{} \times \boxed{} = 54$

3 Match each number to the correct power of 10.

one million 　　　 10000 　　　 ten 　　　 one hundred 　　　 1000

10^4 　　　 10^1 　　　 10^2 　　　 10^3 　　　 10^6

4 Work out the answers to each of these calculations.

a 342 + 789 + 83

b Add together 3942 and 1308

c 3.9 + 4.46 + 8

d 1438 – 759

e Subtract 483 from 951

f 13.6 – 8.94

g 638 × 7

h Multiply 7 by 325

i 3.89 × 4

j   438 ÷ 6   **k**   Divide 952 by 8   **l**   6.72 ÷ 7

5   Here are the prices of tickets for the local cinema.

Weekdays	Saturday and Sunday
Adult £3.49	Adult £4.29
Child £2.75	Child £3.20

a   Mrs Jackson takes her two children to see a film on Wednesday. How much does she pay for the tickets?

b   A family of two adults and four children goes to see a film on Sunday. How much will this cost?

Exercise 12C Revision of Algebra 1

This exercise will help you to revise
- working with sequences and functions
- recognising multiples, factors and prime numbers
- finding squares and square roots and cubes and cube roots

1   Fill in the missing numbers in each sequence.

a   15, 19, 23, 27, 31, _____ , _____   **b**   _____ , 33, 30, 27, 24, _____ , 18

2   Use the rule **subtract 3** to continue the sequence below.

14, 11, _____ , _____ , _____ , _____ , _____

3 Work out the missing inputs and outputs for both function machines.

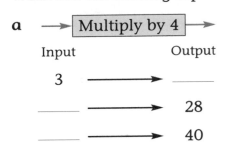

a → Multiply by 4 →

Input   Output

3 ——→ _____

_____ ——→ 28

_____ ——→ 40

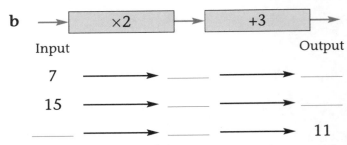

b → ×2 → +3 →

Input   Output

7 ——→ _____ ——→ _____

15 ——→ _____ ——→ _____

_____ ——→ _____ ——→ 11

4 **a** Circle the number that is not a multiple of 4.

4   12   16   26   32   44

b Circle the number that is not a multiple of 7.

21   35   44   56   70   84

5 Write three different pairs of factors for the number 18.

18 = _____ × _____   18 = _____ × _____   18 = _____ × _____

6 Write down all of the factors of 8. _____

Write down all of the factors of 15. _____

What is the **highest common factor** of 8 and 15? _____

7 Circle the prime numbers in the list below.

2   5   9   11   12   15   17   20

8 Write down the answers for each of the following.

a $3^2 =$ _____   **b** $4^2 =$ _____   **c** $7^2 =$ _____

d $10^2 =$ _____   **e** $3^3 =$ _____   **f** $2^3 =$ _____

g $5^3 =$ _____   **h** $9^2 =$ _____   **i** $1^3 =$ _____

9 Find the square or cube root of each of the following.

a $\sqrt{9} =$ _____   **b** $\sqrt{64} =$ _____   **c** $\sqrt{100} =$ _____

d $\sqrt{49} =$ _____   **e** $\sqrt[3]{8} =$ _____   **f** $\sqrt[3]{1} =$ _____

g $\sqrt[3]{1000} =$ _____   **h** $\sqrt{4} =$ _____   **i** $\sqrt{25} =$ _____

Exercise 12D   Revision of Algebra 2

This exercise will help you to revise
- working with terms and expressions
- using rules and formulae
- solving equations
- plotting and reading graphs
- order of operations (BODMAS)

1 Look at the algebra cards below. Circle the three cards which have the same value.

| $3a - a$ | $7a - 4a$ | $a \times a \times a$ | $3 \times a$ | $2a + 2a$ | $a + a + a$ |

2 Simplify each of these expressions.

a $6 \times a$ _____

b $3 \times 2a$ _____

c $3a + a + 2a$ _____

d $7a + 4a + 6b - 3b$ _____

e $n + 2n + 3$ _____

f $3 + 6p - 2 + 2p$ _____

3 The letters a, b and c are used to represent numbers.

a Work out the value of $a + b$ if $a = 5$ and $b = 7$. _____

b Work out the value of $b - c$ if $b = 10$ and $c = 8$. _____

c Work out the value of $5a$ if $a = 9$. _____

d Work out the value of $2a + c$ if $a = 4$ and $c = 3$. _____

4 Selma uses the formula $P = 2x + 2y$ to work out the perimeter of a rectangle.

The letters x and y represent the lengths of the sides of the rectangle.

Use the formula to complete the table.

x	y	P
3	3	16
4	7	
1	8	
3	6	

5 Solve these equations. Show each step of your method.

a $x + 8 = 14$

b $b - 7 = 4$

c $4a = 12$

d $3m + 2 = 11$

e $4a - 1 = 15$

_____

_____

_____

_____

_____

_____

_____

_____

_____

_____

6 Luke and Zoe work out this calculation: **32 − 24 ÷ 4**

Luke says the answer is 26. Zoe says the answer is 2. **Luke is correct.**

Explain why Zoe's answer was incorrect. _____

_____

7 Work out each of these calculations. Remember the correct order of operations.

a $5 + 6 \times 3 =$ _____

b $17 - 8 \div 4 + 5 =$ _____

c $4 \times (5 - 3) + 7 =$ _____

d $18 \div (1 + 2) - 4 =$ _____

e $24 - 4^2 + 3 \times 4 =$ _____

8 The graph shows the line $y = 2x$.

a Complete the table of values for the line $y = 2x - 1$

x	0	1	2	3	4
y					

b Plot the points on the grid and join them to form a straight line.

c What do you notice about the two lines on the graph?

_____

_____

_____

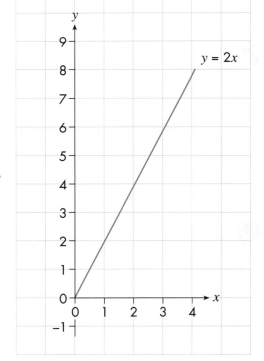

Exercise 12E   Revision of Shape, Space and Measures

This exercise will help you to revise

- recognising symmetry in 2-D shapes
- plotting points in all four quadrants
- finding areas of rectangles, triangles and parallelograms
- finding the sizes of angles in diagrams
- scale drawings
- working with imperial measures

1   **a**   Plot and join these points on the grid (–2, 1) (2, 1) (0, –3).

   b   Name the shape _____

   c   Add any lines of symmetry to the shape.

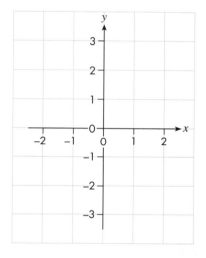

2   **a**   For each shape write down the order of rotation symmetry.

   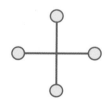

   _____   _____   _____

   b   Circle the shape which has line symmetry.

3   Work out the sizes of angles *a* and *b*.

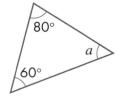

   _____

   _____

   _____

   a = _____ °

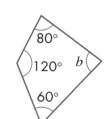

   _____

   _____

   _____

   b = _____ °

4 Which three shapes on the grid on the right have an area of 8 squares?

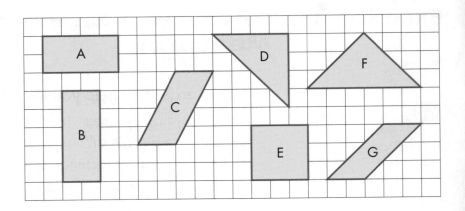

5 Calculate the area of each shape.

a

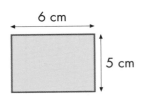

6 cm

5 cm

b

10 cm

8 cm

c

7 cm

5 cm

Area = _____

= _____ cm^2

Area = _____

= _____ cm^2

Area = _____

= _____ cm^2

6 Here is a rule for changing a distance in kilometres (km) into a distance in miles.

distance in km ⟶ | divide by 8 | ⟶ | multiply by 5 | ⟶ distance in miles

Change these distances into miles.

a 16 km = _____ miles

b 80 km = _____ miles

7 This is a scale drawing of a rectangle.

It has been drawn using the scale of **1 cm to 3 cm**.

Measure the lengths and then draw the rectangle to its full size on centimetre-squared paper.

Exercise 12F Revision of Handling Data

This exercise will help you to revise

- constructing and interpreting charts and tables
- finding the mode, median, mean and range of a set of numbers
- working with probability and experiments to investigate probability

1 a Year 9 in Eastpark School have raised £200 for charity through different fundraising activities as detailed in the table below.

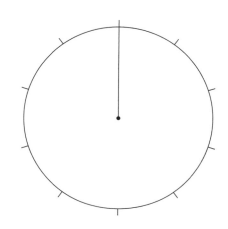

Raffle	£40
Sponsored swim	£50
Non-uniform day	£90
Cake sale	£20

Draw a pie chart to show this information.

b Wesley asked the students in Year 9 which charity they should give the money to. Complete his data collection sheet by filling in the frequency column.

Type of charity	Tally	Frequency
RSPCA	⊥⊥⊥⊤ ⊥⊥⊥⊤ IIII	
Local hospital	⊥⊥⊥⊤ ⊥⊥⊥⊤ ⊥⊥⊥⊤ ⊥⊥⊥⊤ ⊥⊥⊥⊤ III	
Children in Need	⊥⊥⊥⊤ ⊥⊥⊥⊤ ⊥⊥⊥⊤ ⊥⊥⊥⊤ ⊥⊥⊥⊤ ⊥⊥⊥⊤ ⊥⊥⊥⊤ II	
Comic Relief	⊥⊥⊥⊤ ⊥⊥⊥⊤ ⊥⊥⊥⊤ IIII	

c   Draw a bar chart to show this information.

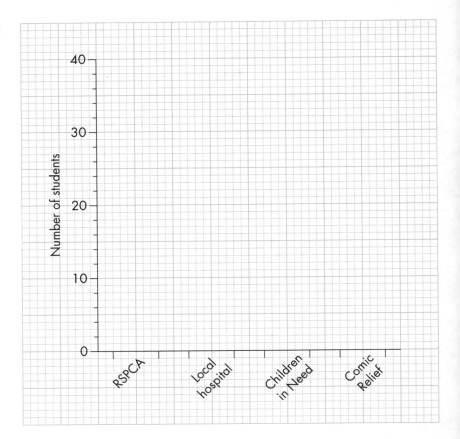

2   The table shows the number of boxes of popcorn sold over one weekend at the local cinema.

	Small	Medium	Large
Friday	25	30	15
Saturday	45	50	30
Sunday	30	20	15

a   How many medium-sized boxes were sold on Saturday? _____

b   How many more small boxes were sold on Saturday than on Friday? _____

c   How many boxes were sold altogether on Sunday? _____

d   How many small boxes of popcorn were sold over the weekend? _____

3   Nicola has used this question in her questionnaire about eating habits.

How many pieces of fruit do you usually eat each week?

none ☐   1–4 ☐   4–8 ☐   8–12 ☐   12 or more ☐

What is wrong with her question? _____

4 Here are some number cards.

| 8 | 7 | 3 | 7 | 5 |

a Find the mode. _____

b Find the median. _____

c Find the mean. _____

d Find the range. _____

e A sixth card is added. **6** Work out the new mean and median.

Mean _____   Median _____

5 Draw and label arrows on the probability scale to mark the probability of each event.

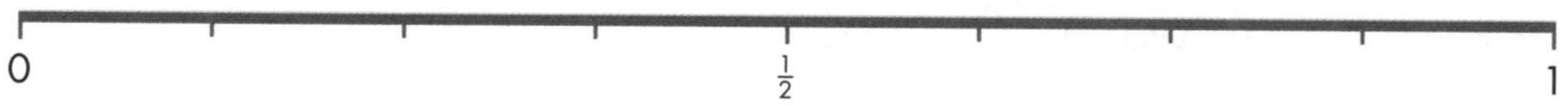

0 ——————————————— $\frac{1}{2}$ ——————————————— 1

a Flipping a coin and it landing on Tails.

b A human being living to be 500 years old.

c Landing on green on the spinner.

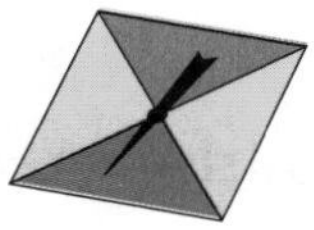

d Picking a circle out of the bag of shapes.

6 If the probability that it will snow on Christmas Day is $\frac{1}{10}$, what is the probability that

it will not snow? _____

7 Ian is going to flip a coin 40 times. He says 'The coin will land on Heads 20 times and on Tails 20 times.'

Explain why he is expecting this to happen. _____

_____

Explain why this may not happen. _____

_____

CHAPTER 13

Handling Data **3**

Exercise 13A Statistical surveys

> **This exercise will give you practice in**
> - choosing suitable data to use in an investigation

1 Jack and his friends want to find out if Year 9 students are interested in having an end-of-year party. There are 200 students in Year 9 altogether. They each ask a different sample.

   a Criticise each sample.

     i   Jack asks 40 boys in Year 9. _____

     _____

     ii Kyle asks two boys and two girls in Year 9. _____

     _____

     iii Anita asks 20 Year 7 and 20 Year 9 students. _____

     _____

     iv Louise asks 20 boys and 20 girls in Year 9. _____

     _____

   b Who do you think would get the most reliable results? Explain why.

   _____

   _____

2 Kwaku has asked 10 students in his class 'How often do you go to the cinema in a year?' Here are the responses:

twice	5	sometimes	7 or 8	4	
a few times	3	1	never	occasionally	

   a Why might Kwaku find it difficult to work with his data? _____

   _____

   b What could he have done to avoid these problems? _____

   _____

3 Imagine that you are going to investigate whether there is a link between a person's hand span and their height. Think about the data you would need to collect.

  a What would you need to measure, and in which units?

  _____

  _____

  b How many people would you use in your sample?

  _____

  _____

  c How would you make sure that you get a representative sample?

  _____

  _____

  _____

Exercise 13B Grouped frequency tables

This exercise will give you practice in

- grouping data into intervals in a frequency table

1 Emily weighed 20 potatoes. Put these weights (in grams) into the grouped frequency table.

| 24.8 | 23.9 | 39.6 | 38.8 | 27.0 | 31.8 | 32.0 | 20.5 | 38.9 | 29.8 |
| 30.3 | 32.7 | 33.9 | 24.3 | 29.5 | 37.9 | 38.6 | 39.4 | 30.0 | 36.5 |

Weight (w) in grams	Tally	Frequency
$20 < w \leq 25$		
$25 < w \leq 30$		
$30 < w \leq 35$		
$35 < w \leq 40$		

2 Wei Lu measured the height, in cm, of 30 seedlings. Record her data in the grouped frequency table.

3.4	1.9	2.8	1.6	1.8	2.3	1.9	2.3	3.1	1.7
1.6	3.2	3.0	2.7	2.7	2.6	2.9	3.1	1.9	1.8
2.5	2.3	2.7	2.6	2.5	1.8	1.6	2.2	3.1	2.0

Height (h) in cm	Tally	Frequency
$1.5 < h \leq 2.0$		
$2.0 < h \leq 2.5$		
$2.5 < h \leq 3.0$		
$3.0 < h \leq 3.5$		

3 Draw an acute angle (less than 90°) on a piece of paper. Measure it accurately to the nearest degree.

Ask 20 people to guess the size of the angle you have drawn. Record your results using a grouped frequency table. You will need to decide which intervals to use, for example $20 < a \leq 30°$, $30 < a \leq 40°$ ...

Angle (a) in degrees	Tally	Frequency

Exercise 13C Which average to use?

This exercise will give you practice in
- working out the mode, mean, median and range for different types of data
- deciding when to use the mode, median or mean

1 Work out the **median** of each set of numbers.

a   12, 14, 18, 22, 30, 42   _____

b   3, 3, 4, 5, 5, 6, 7, 8, 8, 8   _____

c   2.6, 2.8, 4.4, 4.6, 5.0, 5.8   _____

d   39, 40, 48, 57, 61, 65, 68, 82   _____

e   14, 18, 18, 30, 60, 65, 70, 89   _____

2 Here are the weights of seven parcels.

  2.4 kg   1.3 kg   1.0 kg   1.9 kg   1.8 kg   2.7 kg   1.7 kg

  a Find the **median** and **range** of the weights.

  Median _____ kg   Range _____ kg

  b Why would you not use the mode as a measure of the average weight of the
  seven parcels? _____

  _____

3 Here are the weekly wages of five workers in a shop.

  £100   £100   £100   £100   £600

  a Work out the **mode** and **mean** wage.

  Mode _____   Mean _____

  b Which value do you think should be used to best represent the average wage?

  Give a reason. _____

  _____

4 The data in each question is displayed in a frequency table.

  Find the **mode** and **range** for each set of data.

  a

Number of days absent	0	1	2	3	4	5
Frequency	17	6	2	1	3	1

  Mode _____   Range _____

  b

Weight of cake (g)	38	39	40	41	42	43
Frequency	3	7	5	4	1	1

  Mode _____   Range _____

Exercise 13D Drawing and using frequency diagrams

This exercise will give you practice in

- displaying grouped data in a frequency diagram

1 The table shows the amount of time 20 students in the same class spent revising for a test. On squared paper, draw a frequency diagram using the data.

Time (t) hours	Frequency
$0 < t \leq 1$	2
$1 < t \leq 2$	6
$2 < t \leq 3$	10
$3 < t \leq 4$	4

2 The table shows the number of hours of overtime completed by 75 workers in a factory. On squared paper, draw a frequency diagram using the data.

Time (t) hours	Frequency
$0 < t \leq 5$	40
$5 < t \leq 10$	20
$10 < t \leq 15$	10
$15 < t \leq 20$	5

3 The table shows the heights of 40 trees in a wood. On squared paper, draw a frequency diagram using the data.

Height (h) metres	Frequency
$0 < h \leq 1$	2
$1 < h \leq 2$	8
$2 < h \leq 3$	20
$3 < h \leq 4$	10

4 The table shows how long it took 35 students to get to school one morning. On squared paper, draw a frequency diagram using the data.

Time (t) hours	Frequency
$0 < t \leq 10$	15
$10 < t \leq 20$	10
$20 < t \leq 30$	7
$30 < t \leq 40$	2
$40 < t \leq 50$	1

Exercise 13E   Stem-and-leaf diagrams

This exercise will give you practice in
- extracting values from a stem-and-leaf diagram
- displaying a set of numbers in a stem-and-leaf diagram

1 Write down the numbers used in each stem-and-leaf diagram.

a 0 | 7 7 8 9 _____

   1 | 1 1 2 5 5 6 _____

   2 | 0 4 8 _____

b 6 | 3 8 _____

   7 | 2 2 5 9 9 _____

   8 | 3 5 _____

   9 | 4 _____

c 1 | 8 _____

   2 | 4 4 7 _____

   3 | 0 5 6 8 _____

   4 | 2 3 _____

   5 | 0 _____

2 Put the numbers into a stem-and-leaf diagram. The stem is already given in each question.

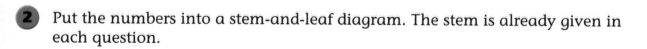

a   38, 43, 45, 46, 46, 49, 54, 56, 58

    3 |
    4 |
    5 |

b   17, 18, 18, 20, 21, 22, 22, 27, 29, 34, 38, 39

    1 |
    2 |
    3 |

c   4, 8, 9, 10, 11, 16, 17, 20, 21, 21, 28, 28, 29, 29, 30

0	
1	
2	
3	

3 Put the numbers into a stem-and-leaf diagram. Work out the numbers you need to use for the stem.

a   75, 76, 76, 79, 81, 84, 86, 86, 88, 89, 90, 94

b   43, 45, 45, 46, 47, 48, 53, 54, 58, 60, 61

4 Draw a stem-and-leaf diagram to show these weights:

38 kg, 38 kg, 39 kg, 40 kg, 45 kg, 47 kg, 48 kg, 53 kg, 57 kg, 59 kg

Exercise 14A   Constructing triangles 1

This exercise will give you practice in

- constructing a triangle when you know the lengths of two sides and the size of the angle between them
- constructing a triangle when you know the sizes of two angles and the length of the side between them

Construct each of the following triangles accurately on squared paper. Remember to label all of the lines and angles. Measure and write down all of the lines and angles shown.

1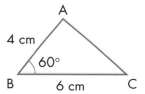

Measure AC = _____ cm

2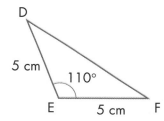

Measure DF = _____ cm

3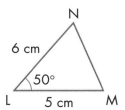

Measure NM = _____ cm

4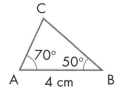

Measure BC = _____ cm

5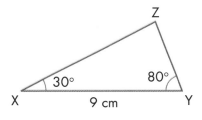

Measure XZ = _____ cm

6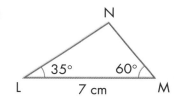

Measure LN = _____ cm

Exercise 14B Constructing triangles 2

This exercise will give you practice in

- constructing a triangle when you know the lengths of all three sides

Construct each of the following triangles accurately on squared paper. Remember to label all of the lines and angles. Measure and write down all of the lines and angles shown.

 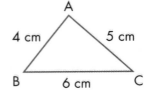

Measure angle ABC = _____ °

 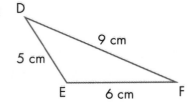

Measure angle FED = _____ °

 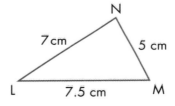

Measure angle LNM = _____ °

Measure angle PRQ = _____ °

 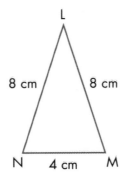 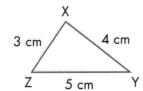

Measure angle NLM = _____ °

Measure angle ZYX = _____ °

Exercise 14C Surface area of cuboids

This exercise will give you practice in

- working out the surface area of a cuboid using the formula for the area of a rectangle
- working out the volume of a cuboid using the formula
  $$2lw + 2lh + 2wh$$

Work out the area of each different face of the cuboid. Use your answers to work out the total surface area of the cuboid.

1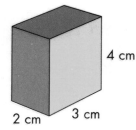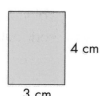

Area of each face $\underline{4}$ cm × $\underline{2}$ cm $\underline{4}$ cm × $\underline{3}$ cm $\underline{3}$ cm × $\underline{2}$ cm

Total surface area = 2 × $\underline{8}$ cm² + 2 × $\underline{12}$ cm² + 2 × $\underline{6}$ cm²

= $\underline{16}$ cm² + $\underline{24}$ cm² + $\underline{12}$ cm²

= $\underline{52}$ cm²

2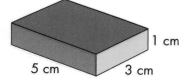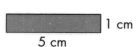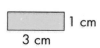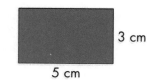

Area of each face _____ cm × _____ cm _____ cm × _____ cm _____ cm × _____ cm

Total surface area = 2 × _____ cm² + 2 × _____ cm² + 2 × _____ cm²

= _____ cm² + _____ cm² + _____ cm²

= _____ cm²

3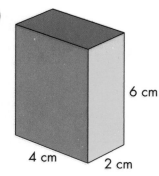

Area of each face _____ cm × _____ cm _____ cm × _____ cm _____ cm × _____ cm

Total surface area = 2 × _____ cm² + 2 × _____ cm² + 2 × _____ cm²

= _____ cm² + _____ cm² + _____ cm²

= _____ cm²

4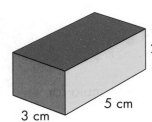

2 cm

5 cm

3 cm

Area of each face _____ cm × _____ cm _____ cm × _____ cm _____ × _____ cm

Total surface area = 2 × _____ cm² + 2 × _____ cm² + 2 × _____ cm²

= _____ cm² + _____ cm² + _____ cm²

= _____ cm²

Exercise 14D Volume of cuboids

This exercise will give you practice in

- using the formula

    Volume = length × width × height or $V = l × w × h$

  to work out the volume of a cuboid

1 Circle the units below that can be used for volume.

m^2 mm cm^2 m^3 cm^3 m km^2 mm^3

2 For each cuboid, write the length (l), the width (w) and the height (h) as a number of cubes. Use your answers to work out the volume of the cuboid.

a
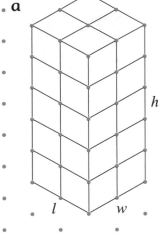

b
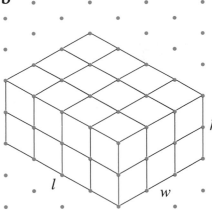

c
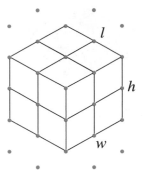

$l =$ _____ $w =$ _____ $h =$ _____

$V =$ _____ × _____ × _____

= _____ cubes

$l =$ _____ $w =$ _____ $h =$ _____

$V =$ _____ × _____ × _____

= _____ cubes

$l =$ _____ $w =$ _____ $h =$ _____

$V =$ _____ × _____ × _____

= _____ cubes

3 Use the formula $V = l \times w \times h$ to work out the volume of each cuboid.

a

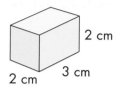

2 cm
3 cm
2 cm

$V =$ _____ $\times$ _____ $\times$ _____ cm^3

$V =$ _____ cm^3

b

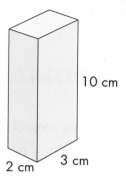

10 cm
2 cm   3 cm

$V =$ _____ $\times$ _____ $\times$ _____ cm^3

$V =$ _____ cm^3

c

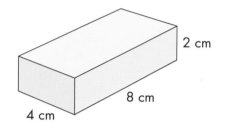

2 cm
8 cm
4 cm

$V =$ _____ $\times$ _____ $\times$ _____ cm^3

$V =$ _____ cm^3

d

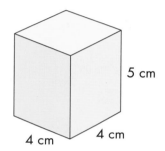

5 cm
4 cm   4 cm

$V =$ _____ $\times$ _____ $\times$ _____ cm^3

$V =$ _____ cm^3

e

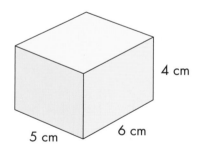

4 cm
5 cm   6 cm

$V =$ _____ $\times$ _____ $\times$ _____ cm^3

$V =$ _____ cm^3

f

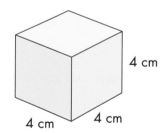

4 cm
4 cm   4 cm

$V =$ _____ $\times$ _____ $\times$ _____ cm^3

$V =$ _____ cm^3

4 Complete the table. Give each answer using the correct units.

l	w	h	V
3 m	5 m	4 m	
12 mm	6 mm	5 mm	
30 cm	40 cm	10 cm	
1 m	5 m	4 m	
15 cm	20 cm	5 cm	

Exercise 15A **BODMAS**

This exercise will give you practice in

- using BODMAS

Do not use a calculator for this exercise.

1 Write the operation that you do first in each of these calculations, and then work out each calculation.

    a $6 \times 2 - 3$ **b** $4 + 3 \times 5$ **c** $12 \div 2 - 3$

    d $15 - 5 \div 2$ **e** $6 \times 2 \div 1$ **f** $4 \times 6 - 3^2$

2 Use BODMAS to work out each of the following.

    a $3 \times 6 + 7$ **b** $8 \div 4 + 8$ **c** $6 + 9 - 3$ **d** $3^2 \times 4 + 1$

3 Use BODMAS to work out each of the following. Remember to work out the brackets first.

    a $3 \times (3 + 7)$ **b** $12 \div (3 + 1)$ **c** $4 \times (6 \div 2)$ **d** $3 + (2 + 1)^2$

4 Use BODMAS to work out each of the following.

    a $16 - 4 \times 2$ **b** $7 \times (4 + 3)$ **c** $12 \div 4 + 8$

    d $(24 \div 4) + 7$ **e** $5 + 3^2 \times 2$ **f** $5 \times 4 - 4^2$

5 Put in brackets to make each of these calculations true.

    a $4 \times 3 + 7 = 40$ **b** $10 \div 2 + 3 = 2$ **c** $5 - 2 \times 4 = 12$

    d $20 - 5 \times 2 = 30$ **e** $10 - 2^2 \times 2 = 12$ **f** $24 \div 2^2 + 2 = 4$

6 Three dice are thrown. They give scores of 2, 4, and 5.

A class makes the following sums with the numbers. Work them out.

    a $(2 + 4) \times 5$ **b** $2 + 4 \times 5$ **c** $4^2 + 5$

    d $4 \times (5 - 2)$ **e** $4 + 5 - 2$ **f** $(4 + 5)^2$

Exercise 15B Adding and subtracting negative numbers

This exercise will give you practice in

○ ordering, adding and subtracting negative numbers

1 The diagram shows a cliff, the sea and sea bed with various objects and places measured from sea level in metres. Use the diagram to answer the questions below.

a How far **above the sea bed** are each of the following?

   i   the submarine

   ii the lighthouse

   iii the plane

b How far **below the lighthouse** are each of the following?

   i   the smugglers' cave

   ii the shark

   iii the submarine

c How far **above** (indicate with a +) or **below** (indicate with a –) **the smugglers' cave** are each of the following?

   i   the plane

   ii the shark

   iii the submarine

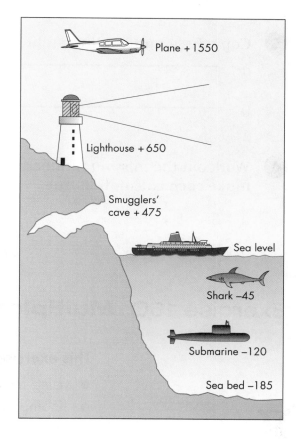

Plane + 1550

Lighthouse + 650

Smugglers' cave + 475

Sea level

Shark –45

Submarine –120

Sea bed –185

2 Five temperatures are marked on the thermometer below.

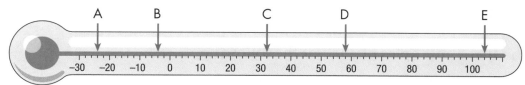

Calculate the difference between each of the following. Remember to give your answer in °C.

a A and B

b A and D

c A and E

d C and E

e B and E

f B and D

3 Copy and complete each of the following.

    a   If +£9 means a profit of nine pounds, then … means a loss of nine pounds.

    b   If +45 m means 45 metres above sea level, then … means 45 metres below sea level.

    c   If −15 minutes means 15 minutes before midday, then … means 15 minutes after midday.

    d   If a train moving forwards at 5 mph is represented by +5, then −5 represents … .

4 Calculate each of the following.

    a $7 - 5 + 6$ **b** $6 - 8 - 3$ **c** $2 - (-5)$ **d** $-2 + (-3)$

    e $-3 - -8 + 7$ **f** $+8 - + 8 + -2$ **g** $-9 - +2 - -1$ **h** $-45 + 89 - 27$

5 Copy these number lines, filling in the missing numbers on each.

    a

         −3   0   2

    b

    −2   0   1

6 Work out the missing numbers from each of the boxes below in order to make each calculation true.

    a $3 + -5 = \boxed{}$ **b** $5 + \boxed{} = 9$ **c** $5 + \boxed{} = 2$

    d $\boxed{} - -6 = 4$ **e** $- 6 - \boxed{} = 3$ **f** $+ 7 - \boxed{} = 4$

Exercise 15C Multiples and factors

This exercise will give you practice in

- using multiples and factors
- finding common factors, highest common factor and lowest common multiple

Do not use a calculator for this exercise.

1 Write down the first 5 multiples of each of the following.

    a 4   **b** 9   **c** 12   **d** 25

2 From the list of numbers below, write down those that are:

    3   7   8   13   14   15   18   24   36   39   45   48   64   69   90   120

    a multiples of 3   **b** multiples of 5   **c** multiples of 4

3 Find the largest number less than 50 that is:

a   a multiple of 3   b   a multiple of 8   c   a multiple of 7

4 Find the largest number less than 50 that is:

a   a multiple of 3 and 4   b   a multiple of 5 and 9   c   a multiple of 2 and 7

5 Write down all the factors of each of the following.

a   48   b   60   c   75   d   130

6 Find the common factors of each of the following pairs of numbers.

a   15 and 24   b   18 and 24   c   28 and 42

Exercise 15D Squares, square roots and powers

This exercise will give you practice in

○ recognising and using squares, square roots, cubes, cube roots and powers

Do not use a calculator for Questions 1 and 2.

1 Write down the value represented by each of the following.

a 7^2 b 9^2 c 11^2 d 13^2 e 15^2

2 Write down the value represented by each of the following.

a $\sqrt{36}$ b $\sqrt{64}$ c $\sqrt{144}$

You may use a calculator for Questions 3–6.

3 Find the value of the square of each of these numbers.

a   19   b   24   c   25   d   32   e   53

4 Calculate each of the following. Give your answers to two decimal places.

a $\sqrt{40}$ b $\sqrt{80}$ c $\sqrt{120}$ d $\sqrt{500}$ e $\sqrt{900}$

5 Calculate each of the following.

    a 4^5 **b** 12^3 **c** 13^4 **d** 21^3

    e 6^6 **f** 7^5 **g** 8^3 **h** 21^2

6 Work out the value of each of the following.

    a   **i** 1^4 **ii** 1^8 **iii** 1^9

    b   **i** $(-1)^3$ **ii** $(-1)^4$ **iii** $(-1)^5$

7 Use your answers to Question **6** to work out the value represented by each of the following.

    a 1^{23} **b** $(-1)^{10}$ **c** $(-1)^9$ **d** 1^{43}

Exercise 15E   Decimals in context

This exercise will give you practice in

- solving real-life problems involving decimals

Do not use a calculator for this exercise.

1 A businesswoman pays five cheques into her bank account. The cheques are for £1456.08, £256.78, £1905.00, £46.89 and £694.58. How much did she pay in total?

2 At the local shop Mary bought two tins of soup costing 57p each, a packet of sugar costing 78p, a loaf of bread costing £1.05, a packet of bacon costing £2.36 and a bottle of wine costing £4.23. What was her total bill?

3 A cake was made using 132 grams of butter, 0.362 kilograms of flour and 96 grams of sugar. What is the total weight of these ingredients in kilograms.

4 Misha's bank account has £467.92 in it. She writes cheques for £67.50, £42.35 and £105.99. How much money will be left in Misha's account after these cheques have been cashed?

5 A quadrilateral has a perimeter of 32 cm. The lengths of three of the sides are 8.23 cm, 3.48 cm and 12.96 cm. What is the length of the fourth side?

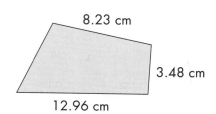

8.23 cm

3.48 cm

12.96 cm

6 William pays a standing order of £55 for fuel each month. Of this £55, £32.78 is for electricity, £12.61 is for gas and the rest is for heating oil. How much does William pay each month for heating oil?

7 A packet of four AA batteries costs £4.15. How much money would you need to buy nine packets of four AA batteries?

8 To make some shelves Mr George orders seven pieces of wood 53.4 cm in length and two pieces of wood 178.5 cm in length. What is the total length of wood ordered by Mr George?

9 A crystal decanter costs £56.32 and a crystal wine glass costs £11.58. How much will a decanter and a set of six wine glasses cost?

10 A table and four chairs are advertised for £385. If the table costs £106, how much does each chair cost?

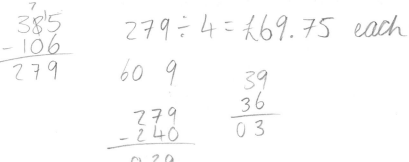

Published by HarperCollins*Publishers* Limited
77–85 Fulham Palace Road
Hammersmith
London
W6 8JB

Browse the complete Collins catalogue at
www.collinseducation.com

© HarperCollins*Publishers* Ltd 2004
10 9 8 7 6 5 4 3 2
ISBN 0 00 717021 1

Helen and Simon Greaves assert their moral rights to be identified
as the authors of this work.

All rights reserved. No part of this publication may be
reproduced, stored in a retrieval system, or transmitted in any
form or by any means, electronic, mechanical, photocopying,
recording or otherwise, without either the prior permission of
the Publisher or a licence permitting restricted copying in the
United Kingdom issued by the Copyright Licensing Agency
Ltd., 90 Tottenham Court Road, London W1P 9HE.

British Library Cataloguing in Publication Data
A Catalogue record for this publication is available from the
British Library

Edited by Jean Rustean
Design and typesetting by Jordan Publishing Design
Covers by Chi Leung
Illustrations by Nigel Jordan and Tony Wilkins
Production by Sarah Robinson
Printed and bound by Martins the Printers, Berwick upon Tweed

The publishers would like to thank the many teachers and
advisers whose feedback helped to shape *Maths
Frameworking*.

Every effort has been made to trace copyright holders and to
obtain their permission for the use of copyright material. The
author and publishers will gladly receive any information
enabling them to rectify any error or omission in subsequent
editions.

You might also like to visit
www.harpercollins.co.uk
The book lover's website